132,133,134

What you should know about DRUGS and DRUG ABUSE

by HARVEY R. GREENBERG M.D.

Four Winds Press/New York

613.8

Greenberg

For Ruth, Matthew, and Paul

The author gratefully acknowledges
the invaluable help of William T.
Beaver, M.D., Associate Professor,
Dept. of Pharmacology, Georgetown
University, Schools of Medicine and
Dentistry, who acted as
pharmacological consultant for this
book. He would also like to thank
the following for sharing their
thoughts on youth and the drug
scene with him and thereby
enriching the book: Paul R. Dince,
M.D.; Mrs. Ruth F. Greenberg;
Edward J. Hornick, M.D.;
Janet Kennedy, M.D.; and
Mr. Jay Kennedy.

CONTENTS

WHY THESE THREE?

Hal, age seventeen, is a senior in a big city high school. Ever since he broke up with his steady girl a few months ago he's felt blue and lonely, and wonders why he was ever born. His parents are away for the weekend; several hours ago Hal swallowed a capsule containing LSD that a friend gave him to "straighten out his head." Now he is in hell; the room is blazing and flames lick at his heels. The people with him are not friends anymore, but devils ready to torture him. The skin on their faces peel off, the naked skulls underneath grin at him. Wild with terror, he runs to the window; he looks down. Eight stories below, as if through a telescope, he sees his girl friend waving to him, hears her calling his name.

Suddenly, he is incredibly happy. Here is the answer, he thinks, as he opens the window and steps out into empty space . . .

Jack, age eighteen, is a freshman at a well-known college.

Tonight he is throwing a party. Everybody is already feeling free and easy on good food, good talk, and the anticipation of what Jack's parties are always known for — Pot! Great things are happening, people are really digging each other, and there never was a better time to turn on. Jack rolls the marijuana cigarettes with a skill that comes with long practice. The pot is part of a very special supply a friend smuggled in from Mexico in the spare tire of his car. There are murmurs of appreciation as the warm glow of the marijuana spreads through the room. "Great stuff," sighs someone.

Jack is a straight B student and looks forward to a promising career in law and a comfortable life. Politically, he's middle-of-the-road. He has no particular axe to grind with the administration of the college. He believes marijuana should be legalized, but doesn't make a big deal out of it. He is also one of those people who seem, so far, to be suffering no ill effects from pot. He was introduced to it by a fraternity friend, and smokes practically every weekend. Sometimes he uses it during the week, or before a rough exam.

At nineteen, Frank is a dead man. He lives a special kind of life centered squarely around heroin.

He is a high school drop-out who has lived in a city ghetto all his life. A glue sniffer at nine, he smoked pot for a while during his early teens. Then, when he was sixteen, his older brother, an addict, gave him his first snort of heroin — and he graduated into the major leagues. A year later, Frank was on the needle, his body requiring several intravenous injections a day. He's had two jail terms for stealing, in order to buy heroin; one stay in the county hospital for skin infections from a dirty needle.

Right now he's shooting up with heroin he got from a new pusher; it is many times "better" than the watered-down stuff he's been used to. It is so "good" that within minutes after it hits his blood-stream, his breathing and heart beat will stop, finishing the death he's been dying most of his life. The junkie who owns the place will really be running scared then; he will call some friends, and at 3 A.M. Frank's body will be dumped in a vacant lot while one guy watches fearfully for a passing patrol car.

What brought these three young people to the drug scene? Hal, the LSD user, was deeply troubled by personal problems and the growing pains of adolescence. Frank's heroin addiction is an illness quite possibly brought on as much by grinding poverty as emotional difficulties. And most experts would feel that Jack, the pot smoker, is not sick at all; he himself certainly thinks his "social" use of one of the oldest drugs known to mankind — marijuana — helps him relax and enjoy life.

What about the effects of these three drugs on these three particular teenagers? The same dose of LSD that was responsible for Hal's death might merely have given another, more stable person — like Jack (or Hal himself at a less difficult time in his life) an enjoyable few hours. On the other hand, the marijuana Jack passed out at his party without so much as a second thought has driven some disturbed young people to the same brink of despair Hal reached on LSD and that others have on heroin. And there are many ghetto youngsters who may try heroin but do not get the high the addict searches for so desperately. And so they don't use it again.

What would the average person's reaction be to these three cases? Would it *really* match the scientific facts?

The account of Hal's death would probably be given widespread publicity as an example of the horrors of drug abuse, despite the fact that the *majority* of people who take LSD do not seem to have such severe psychological reactions.

Jack's ability to lead a seemingly normal life while indulging his taste for marijuana might be proclaimed by an increasingly large number of people as a good reason to legalize this drug. Yet the basic research that would prove or disprove how harmful marijuana really is has not yet been completed.

Frank's death from an overdose of heroin is not spectacular enough to rate headlines in the news. It's a common occurrence in big city slums.

These three cases should give you an idea of the

complicated, and largely unsolved, issues involved in drug use today by teenagers. No matter where you come from, you're sure to have heard something about these problems on TV, from your friends, from your parents, from your teachers. It is not a subject that leads to calm discussion, and very likely a good deal of what you've heard is incorrect, outdated, and distorted by one prejudice or another. Perhaps even the idea of taking drugs frightens you. Maybe you've actually tried marijuana and have some pretty strong ideas of your own. Perhaps, like most kids, you haven't popped pills or used pot, but you *are* curious about drugs and you want to know the facts.

This book will, hopefully, satisfy your curiosity, so that you can make your own decisions based on facts instead of on fear or preaching. It will tell you about the drugs that are commonly in use today and the role they are playing in our society. It will include special reference to the generation gap between parents and their children you've heard so much about. When hard facts are not available, when some claim about drugs is disputed, this book will give you different opinions and indicate which seem to be most reasonable. But remember that knowledge about drugs, about who uses them and why, is incomplete and constantly changing even as this is written. So you owe it to yourself to keep up with things. Read newspapers, current books, and the most recent magazines to help you learn what's happening. (You will find a helpful reading list in the *Bibliography*.)

1

WHAT DRUGS ARE, HOW THEY WORK, AND WHY THEY ARE USED.

Most simply defined, a *drug* is a substance introduced into the body to change the way the body works. A drug's chemical makeup may be simple or very complicated. A drug may be extracted from natural sources, such as plants, berries, or trees, and used in its original state or purified. Or it may be made in the laboratory.

To explain any drug's action, scientists must know about the speed with which it is taken into the body, absorbed into the bloodstream, circulated to body organs, and finally, eliminated.

The way it is given is very important. A drug is usually taken by swallowing, by inhalation, or by injection (beneath the skin, or into a muscle or vein).

Most drugs will work faster when given by injection than by swallowing or inhalation.

A drug may affect one organ principally, such as the brain, or many different organs. Doctors usually give drugs in order to obtain a few specific, desired results, like prescribing aspirin to reduce pain or lower temperature. But often, a drug produces *side effects* that have nothing to do with the result you're trying to get. Side effects are usually not desirable; many people, for instance, get stomachaches with aspirin, because this drug can irritate the lining of the stomach.

The drugs discussed in this book have the power to change feelings, emotions, and, sometimes, behavior; they are *psychoactive*. Scientists have discovered little enough about the way drugs act upon the rest of the body, but they understand least of all how a drug influences the brain and the nervous system. They don't really know what drugs do inside the individual brain cells, so think how hard it must be to measure what they can do to the emotional state of the entire human being! As Dr. Helen Nowlis, a well-known drug expert, has said: "One thing is known with certainty: There are no direct, simple, reliable, cause-and-effect relationships between a drug and any behavior."

There are some factors, however, that definitely determine how psychoactive drugs produce emotional reactions. These factors include: the dose — how much is taken. The route — the way it is taken, and how quickly it gets into the body to reach the brain and nervous system. And afterwards, how quickly it is deactivated and how it is removed from the body. Many psychoactive drugs are deactivated in the liver and eliminated through the kidneys, the bowels, or the lungs. The setting — where the person is when the drug is taken. Is the place peaceful? How many others are there? What are their attitudes toward the drug? What are their attitudes towards the person taking the drug? And the individual himself — what is his emotional state at the moment the drug is taken? What does he expect will happen? Why is he taking the drug at this time? How stable is he to begin with? Is he easily led or influenced? Some people who want to get high badly enough have intense drug experiences after swallowing plain sugar or injecting themselves with water. A friend's telling an impressionable person that a drug will give him a fantastic high may be largely responsible for its effect!

Psychologists believe that certain people are especially likely to get hung up on drugs very quickly. These people appear to be immature. They are easily frustrated by stress; they need kicks constantly and always right away; and they are not able to put off their pleasures for very long.

With all these influences playing a part, you can see why the same drug can affect two people differently, or even the same person differently on different occasions.

Abuse occurs when a drug is taken, usually by self-administration, in a way that departs from approved medical or social practice. The *abuser* wants his drug to produce pleasurable physical and/or emotional sensations, rather than for a medical reason. Sometimes he takes it in such large amounts that it causes physical and/or psychological damage, as well as unusual or antisocial behavior.

All the drugs mentioned in this book can create a state of *dependence* if administered over a long enough period of time. This means that the abuser will experience a sense of need if deprived of his supply. The nature and strength of this need change with the kind and amount of drug abuse.

Physical dependence develops when the tissues of the body get used to a drug, and in some unknown way come to require it in order to continue functioning well. If the drug is then withdrawn suddenly, uncomfortable and even violent physical reactions occur. *Withdrawal symptoms* give a rough measure of how bad a drug habit the abuser has created in himself. Heroin is a drug that may cause strong physical dependence.

Psychological dependence, on the other hand, means that the drug is relied upon to give a pleasurable emotional effect. If withdrawn, the abuser experiences a strong emotional, rather than physical craving for it. However, this can be almost as compelling as a physical need, and in some cases leads the dependent person just as quickly into a life in which seeking and taking drugs is all that matters. Amphetamines (pep pills) are drugs that may cause strong psychological dependence.

Drug dependence may be relatively mild. For instance, coffee contains *caffeine,* and cigarettes contain *nicotine.* These are drugs that produce psychological and even physical dependence (especially in heavy users), but do not lead to the disastrous consequences seen with, say, heroin or amphetamine dependence. (Long-time smokers do, of course, fall prey to lung and heart disease.) You've heard the expression: "I'm dying for a cup of coffee." But no one centers his life around coffee!

The term *addiction,* now falling into disuse, was once used to describe a state of strong physical dependence alone. However, modern drug researchers believe that anyone who becomes so physically or psychologically dependent on a drug that he cannot live usefully without it, whose entire life really centers around seeking and taking drugs, can be called an *addict.*

The condition doctors call *tolerance* occurs when greater and greater amounts of the drug are required to produce the same physical and/or psychological effect.

Some drugs produce tolerance, and physical and psychological dependence, all together; others produce psychological dependence and tolerance only; still others lead to psychological craving alone. Today's experts rate the psychological rather than the physical need for most drugs as more important in causing severe dependency.

"Drug" is a very general term. Actually, there are many different kinds of drugs that affect our feelings in quite different ways. Some excite; others produce drowsiness and calm. Each of the following chapters is about a particular kind or group of drugs: narcotics, sleeping pills, pep pills, etc. In practice, a drug abuser may stick to one drug (like the heroin addict), or may juggle many drugs, according to the effect he's reaching for at any particular time or in any situation. Some abusers have so little sense of self-preservation that they will take virtually *any* drug that promises an emotional or physical effect.

Drugs have been employed to cure sickness and bring comfort since the earliest days of man's recorded presence on the earth. Systematic descriptions of drugs as medicine can be found in Chinese manuscripts three thousand years old. The nonmedical use of drugs — to relieve tension, to get kicks, or to create a state of religious joy and deeper self-understanding — is probably as old as man himself. Many of the drugs that are stirring up such arguments today were known to ancient cultures, and sometimes were just as controversial. Wherever and whenever they have lived, men have pursued the drug experience for several very basic reasons: to soothe the anguish of depression and anxiety, to forget the misery of poverty, to escape from the boredom of everyday life into a relaxed world of instant pleasure. Finally, men have turned to drugs to explore the deepest questions of all: Why am I here? Where am I going? What is life for?

Why should drug abuse present itself as a problem

in America, and for American teenagers, at just this time? Like so many other questions about drugs, the answers are far from simple.

Teenage drug abuse is only part of a serious nation-wide drug problem. Many adults blame teenagers for adult weaknesses. One drug expert after another has pointed out that our adult American society has become incredibly drug oriented. TV advertising nightly urges viewers to pop a pill at the slightest sign of simple nervous tension, and apparently they do what they are told. Almost twenty per cent of the drugs legally prescribed by physicians are sleeping pills, tranquilizers, or stimulants.

Although doctors may overprescribe, rather than take the less popular course of telling patients to rely on their own strength instead of pills, the medical profession can't take the entire blame for drug problems. In a study of families in California, it was found that the average medicine chest contained thirty drugs, and eighty per cent of these had been purchased without a prescription.

If our society is more complicated and stressful than in the past, it is also wealthier, and the differences between the haves and have-nots are more publicized. It is possible that with increasing material comforts and free time, more privileged Americans are turning to drugs to escape boredom. It is also true that our slums are breeding grounds for drug abuse; when the poor are reminded daily of what they can never get, drugs provide for many an illusory and dangerous escape from hopelessness.

WHAT DRUGS ARE, HOW THEY WORK,
AND WHY THEY ARE USED

How widespread really is drug abuse among teenagers? There are few statistics, only general impres-
sions. Arrests for drug abuse of all kinds, especially
for marijuana, have risen in recent years, and for
every arrest there are tremendous numbers of drug
users who are not caught. It goes without saying that
illegal producers and distributors of drugs are not
about to give names and the number of people they
peddle to.

Questionnaires sent to college and high school students do give a very rough idea of the extent of
young people's drug experimentation. From one to
fifty per cent of students, responding to questionnaires sent by researchers to various schools and
colleges, admitted having tried LSD or marijuana,
with high schools reporting the lower percentages,
and less LSD-use compared with marijuana smoking. These questionnaires have pitfalls. The studies
do not cover all of the country, and many students
will not answer such a form at all, even when they
are not required to give their names. Also, such
studies often concentrate more attention on marijuana than on the more dangerous drugs, such as
pep pills and sleeping pills.

However, all available information indicates that
the abuse of mind-influencing drugs, although not
necessarily chronic or heavy, has increased substantially in the past ten years among adults and teenagers alike. There is also a recent alarming rise in
drug abuse by children barely into their teens and
sometimes younger.

There are, of course, different degrees of involvement by teenage drug takers. They can be classified as:

EXPERIMENTERS OR TASTERS — Individuals who have actually tried a drug (usually marijuana) one or more times and haven't had further contact.

IRREGULAR USERS — Those who take drugs occasionally — "just for fun," or in stressful situations, such as cramming for examinations. They generally suffer no physical ill effects, and any dependency they develop is usually psychological and mild. As far as the average teenager in this category is concerned, a drug problem doesn't exist (unless he gets arrested, becomes temporarily ill, or dies). However, some irregular users will become addicted.

HEADS — Those for whom the use of drugs has become the biggest concern of life, who are so hung up that they cannot function adequately without drugs, and whose capacity to live effectively is seriously disturbed for varying and sometimes long periods of time. Strong psychological and physical dependence is regularly found in this group.

Experts agree that the overwhelming majority of teenage drug users belong to the first two groups. This does not mean that even an experimenter cannot be badly harmed by taking a highly dangerous drug just once. It does mean that the number of youths mentally crippled by chronic drug use is relatively small, certainly far smaller than the prophets of doom would have us believe. And, many of these heads are emotionally disturbed to begin with. Were drugs not available, they would very likely turn to other self-destructive activities, such as crime, suicide attempts, or accident-prone behavior.

There are also reasons for drug use that stem from the particular problems adolescents have always had to deal with and resolve: the tyranny of teenage conformity, the pressure to be like everyone else in the group to be "with it" and do the "in" thing. All too often, you may be considered "out of it" if you don't turn on with drugs.

Then there are the fantastic stresses the world places on youth today. At a time when you're changing so fast, the world seems to be changing even faster. So much to learn and master, so many hassles both within and without — college, career, love life; war, peace, overpopulation, the bomb — what does it all mean, and what is it all for? Many young people have said frankly that they wilt at the prospect of joining the rat race their parents seem to be caught up in, where making money and buying things seem to be the only purposes for living and learning. Schools get bigger, more complicated, and further away from the special needs of each student. And who really cares? Drugs can provide an attractive escape from the pain that comes from trying to find a sensible way of living in a time that just possibly may be more troubled than any that ever existed before. Drugs can put a comfortable shield between the teenager and the effort he must make to carve out a place for himself in the world.

Coming to terms with the drug problem must be

accepted as a part of coming of age in many parts of the world today, however negatively adults may feel about it. What you as the next generation will have to contend with no one can begin to guess. But if the past gives any clue at all, youth will continue to be resourceful in meeting and overcoming the challenges that different events and times will provide.

There have been, and always will be, beliefs, customs, and practices over which adults and youth have collided. The most hotly argued belief or custom is one for which there are no clear-cut answers; for which adults, if they are honest, will admit they aren't sure about. And the teenager may artfully use the particular issue in question to prove how completely old-fashioned adults are. The danger exists that parents and children may draw farther apart after a conflict over an issue such as drugs. But it's also possible that the generations still have much they can learn from each other about drugs and about life, so that mutual respect and affection can replace mistrust and anger.

2

TAKE A DEEP BREATH:
THE INHALANTS

When stories first began to circulate that youngsters were getting high by sniffing glue, they were laughed at or dismissed as curiosities. But as time went on, it became clear that *glue sniffing* had to be taken seriously. So did the inhaling of other familiar products, such as gasoline, lighter fluid, paint thinner, nail polish remover, cleaning fluid, spray deodorants, some liquid shoe polishes, and plastic wood! Recently *amyl nitrate,* an inhalant used medically to treat the pain caused by heart disease, has been sniffed to get high.

In the middle of the nineteenth century, scientists discovered that inhaling a gas called *nitrous oxide,* or breathing the fumes of a liquid known as ether, put people to sleep. In that deep slumber they became *anesthetic,* insensitive to pain. Operations that were previously impossible could now be performed without causing the patient to suffer.

But these same inhalants had been known for years to produce a giddy, goofy state. Nitrous oxide was originally called laughing gas. An American dentist, Dr. Horace Wells, first became aware of its anesthetic properties at an amusement show, when someone high on nitrous oxide cut himself deeply without realizing it. And long before it was finally used by surgeons, the stupefying effects of ether were known to chemists. Medical students got high on it at parties called "ether frolics."

The ether and laughing gas fads faded away, and drug abuse by inhalation grew rare — until now, when glue sniffing has become a serious problem.

The mind-influencing drugs found in glue and other inhalants are highly volatile at room temperature, meaning that they pass from a liquid to a vapor quite easily. As vaporized droplets, they are breathed in, passed through the lungs into the bloodstream, and circulated quickly to the brain and nervous system. The most common of these drugs is *toluene,* and there are a vast number of others, including *naphtha, benzene,* and *carbon tetrachloride.*

In this chapter, glue will be discussed at length because it is the inhalant most abused, and because it gives the same kind of high, with similar dangers and side effects, as gasoline or lighter fluid.

The average glue sniffer is likely to be young.

People who sniff glue usually start in their pre-teen years. Although the practice has spread to wealthier areas like the suburbs, most glue sniffing is done in the heart of city slums.

Glue is inexpensive and easily obtained. Sniffing offers the abuser a ready-made escape from a harsh, deprived life, into a world of quickly created daydreams. It is believed that sniffing glue conditions a youngster to use drugs as an escape, so the next step to marijuana or heroin is just that much easier.

Different kinds of glue are used to get high, but the airplane glue used for building models is the most popular. The simplest way glue is taken is by soaking a handkerchief with it. The chronic glue sniffer can take a pull at his handkerchief anywhere, in school, at home, with no one realizing what he's up to. Kids also pour glue into a plastic or paper bag, and place this over the nose and mouth. For fastest results, glue is poured into a shallow pan that is heated to make the fumes rise rapidly. Kids who are habitual glue sniffers may require many tubes a day, but glue is a lot cheaper than most other drugs, so a big habit can easily be maintained. Inhalants are sniffed in private, but also in groups, and these glue parties are striking reminders of the ether and laughing gas frolics of the past.

The effects of sniffing glue are almost immediate, and last for only about an hour. However, they can continue to influence behavior for a day or more. Most users feel drunk, happy, and sometimes extremely powerful. The sniffer may believe that nothing can harm him, and his judgment about his personal safety can become so clouded that serious accidents occur. (Young people who have taken glue have lost their balance while clowning around on a roof top and have fallen to their deaths.) If enough glue is inhaled, the sniffer usually gets increasingly drowsy and finally passes out. Less frequently he becomes restless and overactive. Vivid sexual daydreams may crowd his mind. Aggressive outbursts take place, especially in those who are already emotionally troubled. In a few instances violent crimes, including murder and rape, have been committed under the influence of glue.

Some sniffers pass from a pleasant, dreamy state to a stage of actual *hallucinations* in which they see and hear things that are not really there. These hallucinations may be pleasant — sweet music, beautiful flowers — or frankly terrifying — animals, monsters, devils. The sniffer's body may seem strange to him, his hands and feet feel a mile away. Everyday objects may look as if they've grown to enormous size, or shrink and appear as tiny as if viewed through the wrong end of a telescope. (These extreme psychological effects from glue resemble what happens when drugs like LSD are taken.)

Physically, the stoned sniffer looks and feels dizzy. He is unsteady on his feet, often has a glassy stare to his eyes, and a vacant facial expression. Coordination and balance are likely to be poor. Speech is thick and slurred.

All these physical and emotional effects stem from

the immediate action of glue or other inhalants upon the body, and wear off quickly (for the beginner who takes only a few sniffs). Sometimes the sniffer doesn't even remember what he did or said while high.

As time goes on, sensitive youngsters pass from a stage of experimentation or occasional use to one in which they become true glue heads. This kind of person usually comes from an unhappy family and social background, and starts abusing glue early in his life — in some cases as young as age five. Physical dependence occurs rarely, but extraordinary physiological dependence and tolerance *do* develop. Such a person may eventually have to sniff a half dozen or more tubes of glue to get just one high.

School work, already poor, grows even worse because the user is inattentive and irritable. The glue head's life ends up completely disorganized, with increasing truancy and delinquency. It is a common belief among glue sniffers that their habit leads to insanity; but only rarely does the youngster become so disturbed that he has to be placed in a mental hospital.

In real glue heads, physical symptoms develop that are maintained even when the sniffer isn't high. Glue and many other inhalants are highly irritating to the mucous membranes of the body, so that the eyes grow bloodshot, and the lining of the nose, throat, and lungs becomes inflamed. The breath smells peculiar. Heavy glue users cough frequently, complain of headaches, a bad taste in the mouth, lack of energy, and loss of appetite. In really severe cases, the weight loss may be so great that the sniffer looks as if he had a chronic illness like cancer.

Inhalant abuse over long periods of time can cause serious damage to the liver and kidneys, and possibly, permanent damage to the brain. Tremors (shaking) of the hands, lack of coordination, memory loss, and epileptic seizures (fits) have been seen from time to time in glue heads. These may indicate that the nervous system has been permanently hurt.

Perhaps most shocking of all is sudden death from glue sniffing. Luckily, this is rare. But once the unfortunate victim has died, it makes little difference whether he was an experimenter or a head. Some abusers have passed out with a glue-filled plastic bag over the face and have suffocated. Other deaths have been caused by the lungs suddenly filling up with fluid, or by convulsions. In two cases, youngsters sniffing gasoline were killed when it exploded. Several have been killed sniffing *Freon-12,* a gas that comes in aerosol cans that is used to chill cocktail glasses. Doctors believe that the Freon-12 froze the victims' windpipes, thus cutting off oxygen to the lungs.

For others, death has been slower and more lingering. Some inhalants contain benzene, a chemical that damages the marrow of bones, where the blood cells are made. Benzene sniffers have become severely anemic, and in at least one case, died when the marrow failed to recover. Death from sniffing cleaning fluid containing carbon tetrachloride has also occurred; this chemical fatally damages the liver which is necessary for so many vital body processes.

As always, it is important to distinguish between tasters or experimenters and chronic inhalant abusers. These abusers usually need intensive psychiatric care, not just for inhalant sniffing, but for the underlying personal and family problems that have led them to abuse inhalants.

There are many tasters, but few true inhalant heads. Inhalant abuse apparently reached a peak in the early 1960's. Then, increasing public awareness led to an outcry for legislation to deal with the problem. While it was obviously impossible to prohibit selling everyday household items like shoe polish or lighter fluid, laws have been passed in some states making the sale or possession of glue for the purpose of abuse a crime. A leading glue manufacturer is now putting oil of mustard into model cement to give the abuser a terrifically unpleasant nasal jolt (like the one you get from smelling horseradish) instead of the high he's seeking. Because of the new laws, and because education of the public has made more people aware of the dangers of inhalant sniffing, or perhaps because glue sniffing is simply a fad, inhalant abuse appears to be leveling off at the present time, and it may eventually fade from the drug scene.

3

UP, UP, AND AWAY: THE AMPHETAMINES

What is the kick in pep pills that might lead you to want to try them? They give an intense sensation of excitement, of power and joy. You feel self-confident, alert, and ready to take on the world. As these effects wear off, some people return to a normal emotional state, but others feel let down, tired, and dejected. Often, this state of depression brings with it the desire to pop another pep pill, so that the good times will return. The most popular and widely abused pep pills belong to a group of drugs called *amphetamines*. They are all chemically related to amphetamine, a substance initially produced in the 1940's.

At first, amphetamines were believed to be safe and nonhabit-forming, and soldiers on both sides during World War II routinely took them to stay awake and alert under tiring combat conditions.

Many of these men returned to college after the war, where they continued taking amphetamines to keep awake while cramming for exams. Friends grew curious and tried them too. Since amphetamines seemed so effective, doctors going back to peacetime practice also recommended them frequently. Some former soldiers got hooked completely and they spread their habit throughout the underground drug scene. So by one route or another, the wrong information about amphetamines got around until they became a worldwide menace. At this time, many countries including the United States are undergoing epidemics of abuse.

Like sedatives and tranquilizers, amphetamines are overproduced and overprescribed. At least eight billion are manufactured in the U.S.A. every year, enough to supply every person with about forty doses. Half of all yearly production goes into criminal channels. At anywhere from a dime upwards per pill, there is a huge profit to be made peddling these stimulants on the illegal market.

There are numerous different amphetamines, but their effects are all quite similar. Besides exciting the brain and nervous system, most of them make the heart beat faster, raise blood pressure, and decrease appetite.

For a while, they reduce fatigue and seem to improve lagging concentration, especially on monotonous tasks. But they're no substitute for a good night's sleep. They do *not* restore your performance to the level you're capable of when rested, and when the kick wears off, you may feel even more exhausted than you would have without the drug. So, if you're tired and take pep pills, you run the risk of doing a lot worse than you think. There are many stories of students who thought they had done well on an exam with the help of amphetamines, only to find out they had failed miserably.

Today, most doctors will not prescribe amphetamines to help you stay awake. (Nonprescription pills, such as No-Doz®, contain caffeine, a very mild stimulant also found in coffee, which is only mildly habit-forming.)

Amphetamines are still used for weight control and cases of mild depression, but because of abuse hazards, many doctors believe they should not be given at all for these conditions. Because of abuse, the amphetamines used in inhalers, once commonly available over the counter to relieve nasal stuffiness from colds and allergies, have been replaced by decongestant drugs with less stimulating properties.

Amphetamines have, however, won a place in the treatment of certain types of epileptic convulsions, unconsciousness from sleeping pill overdose, narcolepsy (attacks of deep sleep that last for hours), childhood behavior disorders with overactivity, and Parkinson's disease (a serious illness of the nervous system that produces shaking of the hands and muscular stiffness).

Only a few of the many different amphetamines

are actually used, or abused. The most popular
amphetamines and their trade names are: amphetamine, Benzedrine®; dextroamphetamine, Dexe-
drine®; and methamphetamine, Methedrine® or
Desoxyn®. Preludin®, another relative of the amphetamines, is widely prescribed for obesity and is
alarmingly abused across the world today. Amphetamines also come combined with a barbiturate to reduce the more unpleasant stimulant effects. The best
known is Dexamyl® (Dexedrine® plus Amytal® or
amobarbital).

When used for legitimate medical purposes, amphetamines are usually taken by mouth. This is also
the favorite route of abusers. The intravenous route
is warned against by physicians, but nevertheless
there has been a startling increase recently in
"shooting up" with intravenous amphetamines.
Heads sniff or snort amphetamine powder. Ampheta-
mine-containing inhalers are abused by opening them
up, chewing the wad of cotton or strip of paper
soaked with the drug, or else dipping it in tea, coke,
or water and swallowing the liquid.

Amphetamine tablets (the medical dose is usually
five milligrams) are meant to be taken several times
a day, depending upon the illness. The effect of a
5 mg. tablet lasts about four hours. They also come
in *timed-release capsules,* or *spansules,* that let the
drug into the bloodstream over eight to twelve hours.
Manufacturers package the same drug in different-
colored tablets to indicate different strengths.

Abusers call amphetamines *ups, pep pills, wake*

ups, eye openers, or *truck drivers.* Other slang names come from the trade names, color, shape, or length of actions:

Benzedrine® is also known as *bennies; peaches, roses, hearts* (rose-colored, heart-shaped tablets); *footballs, greenies* (oval-shaped tablets in different colors); *cartwheels, whites* (white, round tablets divided into quarters); *copilots, browns, coast-to-coast* (long-acting capsules, containing mixtures of colored pellets); *bottle, jug, bombido, bombita* (colorless solution, in a vial, for injection).

Dexedrine® goes by the slang terms *dexies, oranges, hearts* (orange, heart-shaped tablets).

Methedrine® is also called *meth; crystals, speed* (in powdered form for intravenous injection).

Tolerance to pep pills is quickly built up by anyone who goes beyond the experimental stage, and it soon takes bigger doses of amphetamine to give the same blast (100-200 mg. or even more). But the body does not develop tolerance for all the other stimulating properties. So, though you require greater amounts to get that same kick, the higher doses make you progressively more nervous, tense, edgy, and sleepless.

Typical physical withdrawal symptoms are not seen if the user suddenly stops taking ups. Although there is some disagreement about this, most experts believe that true physical dependence does not occur. However, the psychological ache for the artificial joys of amphetamines may be as strong a drive to keep seeking them as the worst physical craving.

Experimenters who take amphetamines occasionally and in low doses do not get too many side effects, and an *overdose* is not as common as with sleeping pills. But even a taster can be abnormally sensitive to a small amount or can accidentally overdose himself. When this happens, most of the results come from an exaggeration of stimulant effects. The victim grows restless, over-talkative, irritable, and fearful. He may suddenly become assaultive, even explode into homicidal or suicidal behavior, or get confused and hallucinate. Physical signs and symptoms include nausea, vomiting, dry mouth, diarrhea, chills, sweating, headache, enlarged pupils, high or low blood pressure, chest pain, rapid and sometimes abnormal heart rhythms. Sometimes, death comes from collapse of breathing and heart action, convulsions, or bleeding within the brain.

While tasters may have no particular motivation beyond the curiosity for a new experience, serious amphetamine abusers are in emotional trouble long before they enter the drug scene. The personality of the up head is often similar to that of the abuser of other drugs or alcohol. Indeed, he may have been previously dependent on these drugs, or even still take them. He is said to be immature, can not bear frustration, and has a deep sense of insecurity and ineffectiveness. He prefers amphetamines because with them he feels he can be effective for once in his life. And that he can accomplish things and reach goals that he believes he could not otherwise attempt on his own.

There are several patterns of heavy amphetamine abuse:

THE VICIOUS CYCLE — Overstimulated by amphetamine, the abuser is really burning his candle at both ends. Yet sleep won't come. Insomnia and discomfort mount as he develops tolerance and needs more and more pep pills to feel better. So he takes a barbiturate to sleep, or to get relief from the jitters. (Sometimes other sedatives, or tranquilizers, or large amounts of alcohol, or heroin are used.) But then the sedative really knocks him down, making him depressed and sleepy, even when awake. So he needs even more amphetamine to bring back the high, which in turn leads to a bigger need for downs, and so on. Abusers strung out on barbiturates can get on the same merry-go-round by popping pep pills to wake them out of the sedative slump.

GOOFING ON GOOF-BALLS — Some abusers get a thrill from the combined stimulant and depressant effects of *goofballs,* the amphetamine-barbiturate package mentioned previously. Dexamyl® is the most popular goofball, but some heads make up their own combinations. The goofball enthusiast is not the same as the vicious cycler, who takes pep pills first, and a sedative later on.

AMPHETAMINE JAG — On a jag, the head takes increasingly higher doses of amphetamine with little or no barbiturate to interrupt his thrills. If he's flying on amphetamine by mouth, he may continue to look and feel well for several weeks, but as tolerance builds and he has to take more pep pills, sleep and appetite drop until he is going without rest or food for days on end. Finally, frightened and utterly worn out, he ends his jag by collapsing into a deep sleep that may last for several days straight. The head may tell himself afterwards that he's through with the up scene for good, but soon he usually feels the itch again, and the whole process repeats itself with shorter intervals between jags and more difficulty in coming down (*crashing*) from pep pills.

When amphetamines are taken by the intravenous route instead of by mouth, the effects are so much more intense that the jag is shortened, sometimes lasting a few days instead of weeks. Methedrine® is the amphetamine used for this common and highly dangerous practice, called speeding, which is quickly replacing the LSD trip among drug enthusiasts. Drug experts rate intravenous Methedrine® as dangerous as cocaine. (See Chapter 9.)

Prolonged abuse of amphetamines gives the same physical signs and symptoms already described with overdose: rapid heartbeat, nausea, etc., to which is added extreme weight loss from not eating. Effects persist as long as ups are taken, but usually disappear once they are stopped. Although amphetamines may temporarily seem to increase the sexual drive, heavy male abusers may actually become impotent (unable to perform the sex act), and heads of both sexes can get so worn down from ups that sex becomes unimportant.

More frightening than the physical reactions is the appearance of a characteristic mental state, which, if severe enough, can resemble the severe mental illness *schizophrenia*. Thinking gets disordered. The abuser has frightening aural or visual hallucinations. He believes that people are out to do him harm and becomes highly suspicious or *paranoid*. Normal sounds seem frighteningly loud. Everyday objects are misidentified. A coat piled on a chair becomes a crouched dog about to jump. Mood varies from depression to elation. Suicide attempts or assaults on imagined enemies are common. Judgment is poor, and accidents can happen, especially if the person dares to drive.

What's particularly distressing is that the abuser often realizes that he's going crazy, which only makes things worse. He tries medicating himself with barbiturates, tranquilizers, or heroin to relieve the awful feeling that his world is falling apart. In the worst stage of amphetamine psychosis, the abuser totally loses touch with reality and becomes horribly confused and frightened.

Psychiatrists believe that the pep pill heads who get the sickest were very unstable to begin with; that ups uncover an illness that was probably there all the time, just waiting for the right stress to come along. In their opinion, that is why these mental symptoms may persist long after the pep pills are stopped, and why so many amphetamine abusers become chronically disturbed. Some doctors even believe that prolonged, high-dose amphetamine abuse can permanently damage the brain.

The speed freak hooked on intravenous Methe-

drine® also falls prey to other problems. If he shoots
up with dirty needles he can get severe skin infections or the liver inflammation known as *hepatitis*.
In addition, his body, weakened by lack of sleep and
food, gets so sensitive to speed that he may kill himself with too high a dose. And the speed made in
underground laboratories may be diluted with other
drugs, such as *strychnine* (more dangerous than
speed itself) to make it go further. No wonder, then,
that even the hippies recognize the hazards of Methe-
drine®; their slogan, "Speed kills!" sums up the
dangers very well.

The chronic pep pill head is sick, mentally and
physically, and needs a great deal of medical help.
If he shows severe emotional symptoms he should be
in a psychiatric hospital. But, like the barbiturate
abuser, he is often notoriously untruthful and rarely
tells the doctor about the extent of his dependence.
The amphetamine problem is so widespread that any
physician who's treating a patient with a combination of anxiety, weight and appetite loss, restlessness
and suspiciousness, should always wonder about pep
pill abuse. Highly aggressive or rebellious behavior
that appears out of the blue, for no obvious reason,
should also raise the same question.

In the hospital, all amphetamine is stopped. Pep
pill withdrawal does not have to be gradual, since
severe withdrawal symptoms are not seen. (However, without amphetamine, the patient may get
severely depressed and even suicidal, at least for a
while.) The major tranquilizers, such as Thorazine®,

are very effective in removing agitation and disordered thinking. A nutritious diet with vitamins and
adequate fluids helps to restore health. Intensive
psychotherapy, in and out of the hospital, is often
required, but even with the best care, the abuser may
still return to the drug scene, because he wants the
amphetamine kick more than the psychiatrist's
words. Psychological dependence in confirmed amphetamine abusers, particularly in those who shoot
speed, is very strong. Their cure rate, once dependence is established, is very low.

Pep pills circulated freely for years, but the growing international epidemic of dependency finally has
alerted authorities to start proper action. In this
country, amphetamines and other stimulants are now
officially recognized as *Dangerous Drugs,* and abusing or selling them to others for abuse is punishable
under the same laws that deal with sedatives, tranquilizers, and hallucinogens. (See Chapter 10.)

When it comes to amphetamines, a bit of preaching is allowable. With all the arguments raging about
LSD and marijuana, the amphetamine question often
gets swept under the rug. Yet, many experts believe
that experimentation with amphetamine, so often
begun for harmless reasons, represents more of a
threat to the health of teenagers than all the pot and
acid combined.

4

DOWN AND OUT:
BARBITURATES,
TRANQUILIZERS,
OTHER SEDATIVES

Sleeplessness has cursed man down through the ages, from Biblical days when King Saul needed David's sweet singing to calm his tortured nights, to the present time when insomnia is one of the common complaints that brings people to the doctor's office. Within the past century, drugs have been developed to bring sleep far more effectively than any potion of olden times. When used as directed, these medicines are a blessing, but today they are widely and often dangerously abused. This chapter will discuss *barbiturates,* the best known group of sleep-producing, or *sedative* drugs and other drugs that have similar abuse patterns. Characteristically, whenever a new sedative appears on the market it's hailed for its effectiveness and safety. But people soon discover that this wonder drug has the same dangers and abuse potential as the older sleep medications.

The first barbiturate with strong sedative properties was manufactured at the turn of the century and was called barbital (it's trade name was Veronal®). Since then, hundreds of barbiturates have been created in the laboratory. Of these, ten or so are currently in favor.

Barbiturates are usually given by mouth, although they may also be injected into a muscle or a vein. They are classified according to how fast and how long they work. Popular members of each group with their trade names are also listed below:

Short-acting barbiturates — taken orally, bring sleep in about fifteen minutes, last for two to four hours; pentobarbital (Nembutal®), secobarbital (Seconal®).

Long-acting barbiturates — taken orally, bring sleep in about thirty minutes to one hour; last for about four to eight hours; phenobarbital (Luminal®).

Intermediate-acting barbiturates — taken orally; effects somewhere in between the first two groups; amobarbital (Amytal®).

Ultra-short-acting barbiturates — usually taken intravenously; bring sleep almost immediately, thiopental (Penthothal®).

In drug slang, barbiturates are called *downs, barbs, candy, peanuts.* They are also named according to capsule color:

Amytal® — *blues, bluebirds, blue devils, blue heavens* (solid blue capsule).

Seconal® — *reds, pink, redbirds, red devils, seggies, seccies* (bright red capsule).

Tuinal® (Amytal® plus Seconal®) — *rainbows, tooies, double trouble* (orange and blue capsule). This combination is given to people who have trouble falling asleep and staying asleep. The Seconal® knocks you out, and the Amytal® keeps you down.

Nembutal® — *nembies, yellow jackets, yellows* (solid yellow capsule).

Phenobarbital — *phennies* (various-colored tablets).

Barbiturates slow down the functioning of the brain and other organs, including the lungs and heart. They are therefore called *general depressants*.

Medically, their most common use is for sleeping problems. However, they have also found a place in the treatment of epileptic seizures (they depress the abnormal brain activity responsible for fits). They are used, too, in various medical conditions complicated by emotional stress, such as stomach ulcer and high blood pressure.

Since surgical patients often panic when the mask that delivers anesthetic gas is strapped over the face, barbiturates are useful in putting these patients to sleep before the gas is administered (this is called pre-anesthesia). Ultra-short-acting barbiturates like intravenous thiopental may also be used as the only anesthesia in an operation.

In psychiatry, barbiturates have been replaced by the tranquilizers in treating severe anxiety and tension, but certain ones, such as Amytal®, are still given intravenously to help people recover memories that have been lost as a result of severe emotional shock.

The barbiturates are among the most popular drugs ever created, as far as patients, doctors, and abusers are concerned. It has been estimated that over four hundred tons of them are manufactured every year by almost one thousand companies, enough to give every man, woman, and child in the United States twenty doses or more.

No doubt some busy doctors tend to overprescribe — it's often easier to hand people a pill than to spend time talking with them to find out what the difficulty really is that interferes with their sleep. Just as often, patients don't want to talk, and demand sedatives.

An enormous quantity of barbiturates made yearly never get to doctors. They are sent instead into illegal channels to be sold at great profit for distribution to abusers of all ages.

Mixing barbiturates, sedatives, or tranquilizers with alcohol is another practice on the upswing, with often fatal consequences. Taken together, downs and alcohol add up to more than 1 plus 1. The alcohol and sedative seem to react with each other (the amounts that will be dangerous vary from one person to another) and the total drug in the package exerts a stronger effect than the body can take. This leads to slowing and collapse of breathing and of heart action. Death can follow quickly.

What kind of kick is the barbiturate abuser after? He usually wants more than a good rest, although the escape of sleep (literally hibernating from your troubles) can seem very attractive to the easily frustrated individual who gets hung up on drugs. The down head seems to get the same effects others find with alcohol, but stronger. Barbiturates provide a dreamy, drowsy feeling of happiness, or *euphoria*. Like alcohol, they also temporarily make the user suspend his usual judgments about himself and what he's allowed to do. For instance, a boy who's anxious about sex may feel less guilty or shy on downs, freer to approach girls. Or if he's generally isolated and quiet, downs can make it easier for him to come out of his shell socially. Less often, a person who rigidly controls his angry or aggressive feelings when he's straight, may get irritable and bad-tempered while stoned on barbiturates.

The typical barbiturate-dependent person is often the same personality type as other drug heads. He is immature, intolerant of the usual life stresses, and needs kicks all the time. His father is often found to be weak or not around very much, and his mother may appear confusingly inconsistent — overindulgent, spoiling him, and yet sometimes rejecting him.

Doctors say that a person who has a history of dependence on other drugs — especially alcohol — also is very likely to become involved with barbiturates. In fact, many barbiturate abusers also rely heavily on pep pills, other sedatives, and tranquilizers. The reverse also holds true. Abusers of other drugs often enrich their pill diet with downs for a change of pace. In one study of heroin addicts, twenty-three per cent admitted to dosing themselves with barbiturates; they especially turn on to downs during a *drug panic,* when their supply of heroin runs short.

A person stoned on barbiturates looks and acts drunk. His speech is slurred, he staggers when he walks, he frequently loses his balance and falls. He gets drowsy, his head nods, and he passes out. His mood is usually high and goofy, but as noted before, he can suddenly become quite irritable and quarrelsome.

A heavy daily intake of barbiturates quickly leads to tolerance, psychological dependence, and physical dependence, or addiction far worse than with heroin. The usual medical dose of barbiturates for sleep is 100 mg. at bedtime. (A milligram is 1/1000th of a gram. It is a metric unit of weight.) While there are wide variations in daily abuse, experts state that about 600 mg. per day for several weeks are required to become really hooked. (The usual barbiturate capsule contains 100 mg.)

The continuous heavy abuse of barbiturates can lead to very serious damage of mind and body, which some doctors believe may be permanent. The heroin addict neglects himself and descends the social ladder because of the time, effort, and expense involved in keeping himself supplied with his drug. But a

barbiturate head usually does not have to spend as
much on his habit (downs can be bought for a nickel
to a dollar per pill) as the heroin head. The decay of
personality, personal hygiene, and social habits are
directly related to the fog he perpetually lives in.
Fantasy replaces reality and the abuser may even
become *psychotic*. He hears voices, sees things that
aren't there, doesn't know where he is or what time
it is, and keeps growing more confused and fearful.
Such a state is called *delirium* and requires urgent
medical care.

Typically, the down abuser is reluctant to tell a
doctor about his dependency, and if he does, he generally lies about the amount he's taking, giving the
impression he's on a low dose. His life is endangered
by this secrecy, especially if he is hospitalized for
some other medical condition, loses contact with his
supplier, and does not let anyone know about his
problem.

Characteristically, on the first day of withdrawal,
the abuser grows nervous, feels weak, nauseated, and
restless. As night comes, he can't sleep, his blood
pressure drops, he sweats profusely. By the second
day he may have epileptic-type seizures. If he is not
treated vigorously at this point, he can die. Between
the third and seventh day after withdrawal, the emotional symptoms of delirium — panic, confusion, and
terrifying hallucinations — appear, although they
sometimes occur earlier.

Untreated, the withdrawal picture lasts nearly a
week. While many down heads go off barbiturates

far away from doctors and hospitals, withdrawal is a painful and potentially life-threatening illness. The head is literally gambling with his life if he tries to do it alone.

Doctors treat barbiturate withdrawal first by finding out how much has been taken every day. If the patient will not tell, is not obviously drowsy, and looks jittery and tense, he will be given test doses of a barbiturate like Nembutal® until he shows signs of drug intoxication, such as drowsiness. Doctors are able to figure out how much of the drug the person has been taking daily from the amount needed to bring him down. Once this estimate has been made, the patient is put on his usual daily dose and then slowly withdrawn, usually at ten per cent of his daily habit each day, or even more slowly.

If recovery seems unusually long, or if the person is drowsier than he should be, doctors suspect that he is hiding extra pills or having downs brought in by friends. Restricted visiting and frequent searches of his belongings may be necessary.

During this time, the abuser is given a good diet with plenty of vitamins and fluids, and observed carefully for seizures. For most chronic barbiturate-dependent people who maintain a habit of 1,000 mg. per day, the time for withdrawal is about ten days, using the ten per cent method. After he is completely clean, the abuser often feels irritable and sleepless for a few more weeks.

This period is a good time to discuss the possibilities for professional help with his problems. These people usually need long-term psychiatric care, but often they resist treatment, will not follow advice, and despite the severity of their withdrawal symptoms, return to downs after discharge from the hospital.

Accidental or suicidal overdose of barbiturates is an even more serious medical emergency. Some idea of the barbiturate danger comes from the frightening statistics on death through overdose. Each year, three thousand Americans are killed by taking these drugs, either accidentally or on purpose. Many abusers do away with themselves unintentionally; after swallowing a few downs, the person's mind is so befuddled that he forgets how much of what drug he took. Ultimately, ignorant of his tragic mistake, he overdoses and dies.

If the patient has taken a large amount of downs he is usually brought to the hospital in *coma,* a deep state of unconsciousness from which he can not be awakened by shouting or shaking. In truly deep coma, the vital functions are slowed down tremendously, and as blood pressure and breathing rate drop, the patient is literally at death's door. The amount of urine produced by the kidneys also decreases, and the functioning of the liver is disturbed. Since barbiturates are normally changed by the liver into harmless chemicals and then eliminated from the body through the urine, the patient in coma has just one more strike against him. So, in addition to pumping out the stomach to remove undigested barbiturates, doctors may hook the patient up to a mechanical (artificial) kidney, which does what his own kidneys can not: wash the blood clean of drugs. The introduction of this machine in the past twenty years has been responsible for saving hundreds of lives.

In less serious cases, where the patient swallows only a few pills and is mildly sleepy, the artificial kidney is not necessary, and with proper medical support the body will pass out the barbiturates on its own within a few days.

NON-BARBITURATE SEDATIVES

Many drugs both new and old besides barbiturates are given by doctors for sleeping problems and are misused widely, either alone or in combination with other sedatives, pep pills, and tranquilizers.

Two medications that have been occasionally abused through the years are *chloral hydrate* and *paraldehyde,* but some of the recently manufactured sedatives are taken for kicks much more commonly than are the older ones. These include Doriden® (drug slang: *goofers, cibas*), Placidyl®, Noludar®, and Valmid®.

Each produces tolerance, psychological dependence, and physical dependence in varying degrees. Withdrawing from them suddenly after heavy abuse leads to the same dangerous physical and mental symptoms seen with barbiturates. Accidental or suicidal overdosage with coma and death have also been reported, especially with Doriden® and Placidyl®.

The medical treatment for severe dependence consists of well-supervised, step-by-step withdrawal of
the drug, or else substitution of a barbiturate like
Nembutal® equal to the amount of nonbarbiturate
sedative taken daily, then withdrawal of the barbiturate step by step. Psychiatric therapy for the emotional conflicts that have led to the abuse of these
drugs is also usually necessary.

Sedatives sold over the counter are occasionally
abused, but produce only mild psychological dependence. Medicines such as Nytol®, Sominex®, and
Sleep-Eze® contain a combination of ingredients: an
aspirinlike agent — salicylamide, an antihistamine,
and in the case of Sominex® and Sleep-Eze®, a drug
called *scopolamine*. None of these is a true sedative
of the barbiturate type. Salicylamide, in addition to
being a pain-killer, supposedly has a small calming
action. *Antihistamines* are used medically to fight
allergies, and have some sleep-producing activity on
the side. Scopolamine is employed in surgery as a
mild sedative in combination with other agents for
pre-anesthesia and anesthesia. It is discussed further
in Chapter 6 because of its hallucinogenic potential.

MINOR TRANQUILIZERS

These drugs, developed within the past fifteen
years or so, are tremendously popular today. The
three best known are Miltown® (also known as meprobamate, or Equanil®), Librium®, and Valium®.
They are prescribed not for sleep, although they do

possess mild sedative action, but for anxiety and tension. They are sometimes termed *minor tranquilizers* because they are not very good at helping the overwhelming anxiety that occurs with really severe emotional problems. For this, doctors give *major tranquilizers* like Thorazine®, a group of drugs rarely, if ever, abused.

These minor tranquilizers are among the most overprescribed drugs in the U.S.A. They are often taken for simple everyday difficulties that should be resolved without drugs.

The minor tranquilizers, especially Miltown®, have an abuse hazard almost as serious as the sedative group. The history of Miltown® with regard to dependency is quite similar to that of the barbiturates. When first introduced it was supposed to be safe, without psychological or physical dependence, or withdrawal symptoms. Then, reports of tolerance and dependence began to appear and soon a severe withdrawal state with convulsions was seen in Miltown® heads. Finally, experts recognized that Miltown® was not a harmless drug, and that it should be given with great caution. The same kind of person who gets kicks from barbiturates or alcohol will often find the minor tranquilizers ideal, although why one person would get a better high from Miltown® or Librium® than from a barbiturate is not really understood. In practice, abusers often get hooked on a mixture of sedatives and tranquilizers.

The treatment of minor tranquilizer dependence is the same as for a nonbarbiturate sedative habit. The doctor finds out how much tranquilizer the abuser is taking daily, makes sure he gets that amount to start with in the hospital and begins gradual withdrawal following the ten per cent rule. Many doctors favor substituting an equivalent amount of barbiturate like Nembutal® for the tranquilizer or tranquilizer-sedative mixture the head has been dosing himself with, then slowly withdrawing it.

As with the sedatives, there is much illicit underground traffic in Miltown®, Librium®, and Valium®. Although, at this writing, they have not yet been classified as Dangerous Drugs, it is hoped that eventually, like barbiturates and the nonbarbiturate sleeping pills, they will become increasingly subject to more effective legal controls. (See Chapter 10.)

5

STILL GOING STRONG: ALCOHOL

Isolated groups of drug sophisticates put alcohol down. Hippies and turned-on college students say drinking is an inferior trip, compared to the liberating pleasures of pot, acid or speed. But this part of the drug-taking population certainly doesn't speak for the rest of the world. Alcohol continues to be the most sought after, easily obtained, used, and abused drug in the English-speaking world. It is also the only drug besides nicotine (in cigarettes) that is specifically forbidden to teenagers by most state laws, but permitted to adults. You can get a good idea of the popularity of alcohol in the United States from the fact that more than ten billion dollars a year are spent on liquor. About seventy per cent of American adults take at least one drink a year, and the figures for teenagers who have sampled alcohol at least once are almost as high. Seventy million Americans drink regularly, ranging from small amounts to chronically heavy consumption. Drinking, by those who can handle it, is considered an enjoyable way to relax. For those who cannot, it may be a nightmare.

Throughout history, an uneasy distinction has been drawn between drinking that is supposedly harmful and drinking for social or medical reasons. But whatever the reasons man gives himself, he has always been greatly attracted to alcohol. And every society has learned to brew its own favorite.

The drug in any alcoholic drink that makes a person feel good or bad, is *ethyl alcohol*. In its purest form, this is a colorless liquid with hardly any odor, and a stinging taste. Alcoholic beverages are made from the fermentation of fruits, vegetables, or grains and contain up to fifty per cent ethyl alcohol.

There are other alcohols besides ethyl alcohol, but they are not popular. Some are very dangerous. Wood, or methyl, alcohol causes blindness and even death; during the days of Prohibition, epidemics of wood alcohol poisoning from bootleg liquor were common.

Although some alcohol gets into the bloodstream by sniffing, most enters through the stomach and small intestine. The more food in the body, the more slowly alcohol gets in. That's why a person who drinks on an empty stomach gets high so quickly.

About ten per cent of the alcohol you drink goes

out unchanged through the kidneys and lungs. (Alcohol on the breath is traditionally a sign of heavy drinking, but this is completely unreliable.) Ninety per cent is burnt up by the body's "power plant" and chemically converted into energy, as is food, although doctors point out that drink is no way to get adequate nourishment.

Alcohol starts to work in a few minutes. An average "dose," one shot of whiskey or one bottle of beer, influences a person for several hours, but the more he drinks, the longer alcohol's effects will last.

Alcohol is not an important source of fuel to keep the body running. Its principal effects are on the nervous system and brain, where is acts as a *depressant,* like anesthetics and sedatives.

Among the first brain functions to be slowed down by alcohol's depressant action are the higher centers that control complicated thinking and regulate the emotions. Alcohol relaxes inhibitions and conscience. But the popular notion that alcohol increases sexual performance is a fairy tale.

The overactive behavior that some people show while drinking makes it seem as if they are being stimulated by alcohol, but what's really happening is that the higher centers that normally would control this behavior have been temporarily put out of action.

That good, warm sensation a person feels inside when he's been drinking is caused by an increase in the amount of blood flowing through the stomach, hands, and feet. It is mistakenly believed that alcohol can be helpful if you're chilled. Actually, it is responsible for more rapid loss of body heat, and also increases sweating, which may make you even colder. Using alcohol to keep warm outside in freezing weather is both foolish and dangerous.

Although a person may *feel* stronger or mentally sharper after several drinks, it has been proven that the body's functioning is actually decreased by alcohol. Familiar tasks may be carried out more easily than work that requires skill and close attention, but any sudden change in the world around a person may ruin his ability to do even routine jobs well. This is why anyone is such a menace if he drives while drunk.

At higher doses of alcohol, the depressant effects really begin to take over. People get clumsier, stagger when walking, slur speech, and finally grow drowsy and pass out. In rare cases, such as that of children in accidental poisoning, or adults who chug a fifth of whiskey, enough alcohol gets into the blood to knock out the parts of the brain that control breathing and heart beat, and death comes swiftly.

There are other reactions produced by alcohol. It stimulates the flow of saliva in the mouth and digestive juices in the stomach and makes the kidneys put out more urine. This is why people may have to go to the bathroom more frequently when drinking.

Modern doctors hardly ever prescribe alcohol. Probably its most important use in medicine today is as a liquid in which to dissolve other drugs, and to cool down the skin of patients with high fevers.

Occasionally, physicians will inject alcohol into a nerve to kill pain, or will give a drink before meals to elderly or convalescent patients to improve appetite and to raise spirits.

ALCOHOLISM

Alcohol does more damage than LSD, marijuana, and heroin combined. As far as the teenage drug scene is concerned, alcohol is rated at least as much of a problem, if not more, than the abuse of any of the other drugs hitting the headlines today.

Half of all fatal crashes and a high percentage of nonfatal auto accidents involve drinking drivers; thirty per cent of the pedestrians killed by cars are "under the influence." Alcohol is also held a contributing factor in thirty to forty per cent of other violent deaths, including suicides and homicides.

At what point does social drinking leave off and a true drinking difficulty begin? How and when can someone say for sure that he isn't handling drinking well? A skid row wino is easily recognized, but the majority of problem drinkers don't fall into this category.

Experts estimate that five to six million adults in our country (and probably thousands of teenagers) are afflicted with *alcoholism*, making it the fourth most important public health problem today, following mental illness, heart disease, and cancer. Nearly 250,000 Americans become *alcoholics* each year.

And for every alcoholic, five or six other people

related by family or business ties are also seriously hurt. When one or both parents drink to excess, there is a high rate of divorce, desertion, and mental and physical cruelty. Children of alcoholics frequently become delinquents, criminals, or suffer from emotional illnesses, including alcoholism. The cost to industry through ineffectiveness and absenteeism runs into several billion dollars a year.

Research into alcoholism is complicated by the preaching, disgust, and contempt so often directed at drinkers. It is only recently that alcoholism has been thought of as a sickness, and it's still hard for many people to grasp this fact. Some experts still view alcoholism as a moral or spiritual problem rather than a medical one. So there have been conflicting definitions of what alcoholism really is.

According to Dr. Morris Chafetz, a well-known expert in the field of alcoholism, the alcoholic suffers from a behavior disorder that makes him get involved with drinking to the point where both his physical and emotional health are harmed. He loses control of himself in many ways once he starts to drink. Self-destructive attitudes are exhibited in personal relationships and various life situations.

Dr. Chafetz zeroes in on the central feature of the alcoholic's life style: his capacity to hurt himself in dealing with other people, to set up situations where he always loses out, on *or* off the bottle.

This definition covers the different types of disturbed drinkers without relying on meaningless standards of what's "too much" alcohol consumption.

The illness of the alcoholic is not measured simply by the amount he drinks, but by his despair, frustration, guilt, and self-hatred.

There is not one simple type of alcoholic personality. From the mental health point of view, problem drinking is a symptom, like fever. Fever can come from many sources: flu, pneumonia, a ruptured appendix. And serious drinking difficulties stem from many kinds of life stress, conflict, and disturbed inner feelings. Alcoholism occurs in adults and teenagers who vary remarkably in background and in basic psychological strength and weakness.

Male alcoholics are said to outnumber women by about five to one, but this figure is disputed. It may be easier for the woman alcoholic to escape detection than for a man.

Although there is not a specific type of adult or teenager who relies heavily on alcohol, experts believe that those with serious alcohol problems cluster into two broad groups, called *reactive* and *addictive*.

Reactive alcoholics are drinkers who are reacting to a well-recognized life stress, such as death, or the sickness of a loved one. Prior to the onset of heavy drinking, the reactive type often has a good school or work record, and gets along well with people. But once he finds relief with alcohol, he keeps returning to it, until he grows so dependent that he can stop drinking only with great effort, usually after the stress has let up. When he goes on a binge, the reactive alcoholic indulges heavily. Afterwards he may stay sober for months or even years, or else re-

turn to a lower and more socially accepted level of
drinking. But, in some cases, he gets so attached to
alcohol that he cannot stop, and his entire life revolves around drinking.

The addictive alcoholic had a sick personality long
before he takes his first drink. His relations with
others have always been poor. As a teenager, his
school grades were apt to have been low, and he
may have had dating problems. When he grows up,
he is not very good as a worker, and he changes jobs
frequently. Marriage is stormy and unhappy; divorce is frequent. The behavior of the addictive
drinker is so disturbed, angry, and self-destructive,
whether sober or drunk, that he is the one society
identifies as sick.

Addictive drinkers often start as teenagers, and
from the start show a deep abiding interest in alcohol. They drink most of the time, and may stay in a
mildly intoxicated state. Unlike the reactive alcoholic, however, the addictive person's binges do not
seem to be related to any cause like a death or dis-
appointment in love. They stop drinking simply because they are too sick or too broke to continue.

Some psychologists believe that every alcoholic is
a depressed and bitter person who has been over-
indulged and coddled in childhood. As he grows up
and meets frustration, he reacts with intense resent-
ment and is overwhelmed by helplessness. He makes
enormous demands for love and attention, yet somehow believes he can not get what he needs or else
feels it is never enough. His social contacts are empty

and unrewarding, and his sex life is guilt-ridden and unhappy. Filled with despair and mistrust, he strikes out at others and at himself by excessive drinking.

The bottle satisfies his need for warmth, but only for a while. The more he drinks, the more depressed, worthless, and angry he feels. So a vicious circle is set up, with ever more drinking, loneliness, and fear feeding on one another.

Alcoholics often grow up and identify with significant adults, usually one or both parents, who themselves have shown a preference for dealing with life's problems by drinking. Study after study demonstrates a high rate of alcoholism in the family background of the problem drinker.

Other scientists look beyond psychological factors and believe that the alcoholic craves drink because of disturbances in his physical functioning. According to one such theory, alcoholics can not break down sugar into energy the way normal people do, and need alcohol as an extra energy source. There are many other such physical theories, but to date not one of them has been proven. There is no doubt, however, that abusing alcohol for prolonged periods of time does create physical changes in the body, with serious effects in many cases.

The studies of social scientists indicate that societies in which alcohol use begins early, in a family setting, and where there is no particular shame associated with drinking, usually do not have a big drinking problem.

Alcoholism flourishes in the same atmosphere of

poverty and misery as so many other forms of drug abuse. It is also widespread where there is great turmoil and suffering, as in time of war.

How does alcohol compare with other drugs as far as dependence or addiction go? Obviously, the alcoholic has a strong psychological dependence on drink to make his life brighter. Tolerance also develops, but takes longer to build up than with drugs like the barbiturates or narcotics, and is not as marked as with heroin or morphine. Some degree of physical addiction also can develop. Most chronic alcoholics who have grown tolerant require three to four times the amount taken by an occasional drinker to get drunk, and will get some physical discomfort if they suddenly "go on the wagon." But there are others who handle withdrawal fairly well (unlike heroin addicts, who *always* have withdrawal symptoms).

What are the effects of prolonged heavy drinking upon the body, mind, and personality?

Chronic alcoholics often are ill, and may not live as long as nondrinkers or people who drink in moderation. Alcohol donates calories to the body, and cuts both appetite and food intake down. The average alcoholic may get half or more of his daily caloric requirements from his drinking. If he goes on for many years, his body will be chronically starved for the protein, vitamins, and minerals he needs, and various organs, such as the liver, may be hurt. (*Cirrhosis,* a serious illness marked by shrinking and scarring of the liver is much more common in alcoholics than in people who do not drink.)

Alcohol has an irritating effect on the membranes of the throat and stomach. So it is not unusual to find heavy drinkers complaining about sore throats and digestive upsets. Alcoholics have a higher rate of stomach ulcers with bleeding, than nondrinkers.

Alcoholics also tend to fall ill more often from infectious diseases like tuberculosis and pneumonia. This seems to be due to poor personal care rather than to alcohol itself.

There is ample evidence that chronic alcoholism can cause damage to the brain and nervous system. Some very heavy drinkers may develop symptoms like numbness and weakness of arms and legs, double vision, loss of memory, and personality changes, to name only a few. This kind of damage is less frequent with alcoholics who manage to eat reasonably well and get a fair supply of vitamins in their diet.

Delirium tremens, or *DT's,* seen in chronic alcoholics who are over thirty, but sometimes younger, is a well known illness of the nervous system associated with alcoholism, and may occur after a prolonged bout of heavy drinking, and may be due to stopping alcohol suddenly, when the money runs out, or to injuries and infections. The alcoholic with DT's is restless, frightened, and confused. He sees terrible visions—monstrous animals, bugs crawling over his skin; his hands shake uncontrollably; he runs a very high temperature and sweats tremendously. DT's is a medical emergency and without proper treatment, ten per cent or more of its victims will die from heart failure, convulsions, or complications like pneumonia.

HELPING THE ALCOHOLIC

There are many different ways to reach the alcoholic. Every sufferer is unique, so treatment should be individualized to meet the particular problems and needs of each patient. Whatever the method employed, a positive relationship with people who will care for him, be firm, yet try to understand without judging or putting him down is most helpful. If he is dismissed contemptuously, the chances for future rehabilitation may be ruined.

The severely drunken person is actually suffering from a drug overdose and requires intensive medical care — just as with any other drug overdose. Treatment includes sedatives or tranquilizers to calm the anxiety that started a drinking bout or that develops after stopping alcohol; adequate food, fluids, and vitamins; attention to his overall physical condition to make sure he is not suffering from the diseases that come with heavy drinking, and — above all — treatment with kindness and respect.

Psychiatrists are in short supply, so the family practitioner is often the chief source of medical help. Many problem drinkers can do quite well with sympathetic doctors who see them regularly and listen to their problems, while attending to their physical needs.

When the mental health professional does treat alcoholism, several approaches are available. The psychiatrist may see the patient several times a week over many years to probe deeply into his past and discover the childhood hassles that may have led the patient into drinking. But many alcoholics do not tolerate this; they are people who need a great deal of help in managing their present life. With patients like this, the doctor may choose a more active, encouraging position. Psychiatrists often see the parents, wife, and children of the patient too. Or family members may be counselled by a skilled social worker.

Group therapy has also been used successfully. Small numbers of patients meet regularly to discuss their difficulties in the presence of a trained therapist. In the group, the alcoholic learns to see himself as others see him, so that his distorted self-image can be corrected.

There are two important physical treatments for alcoholism. Antabuse® is the trade name of the drug *disulfiram*. It changes the way alcohol is broken down by the body, so that instead of being converted into harmless waste products, a substance called *acetaldehyde* is formed. This causes an extremely uncomfortable physical reaction within a half hour after drinking: reddening of the skin, coughing, vomiting, and severe nervousness. The alcoholic takes Antabuse® every day and is conditioned by the bad effects of drinking while on this drug to stay away from the bottle.

In *aversion therapy,* the alcoholic is trained to associate drinking with an unpleasant physical sensation too. Shortly after taking alcohol, he is given a drug to make him vomit. After several of these aversion sessions, the alcoholic is conditioned to associate drinking and vomiting. Or else he is given an electric shock every time he reaches for an alcoholic drink.

Alcoholics Anonymous, or AA, is a voluntary self-help organization formed by alcoholics. AA furnishes its members with many of the supports of group therapy. The new member comes to regular sessions where he hears other drinkers speak openly of their problems and tell how they overcame them. If he slips, an AA member can be at his side in moments to get him whatever help he needs. AA also runs a program for the teenage children of alcoholics, to discuss the difficulties of living with an alcoholic parent. The program is called ALATEEN. (For further information see *Help: Treatment Centers.*)

As with any chronic illness, the individual with alcoholism is almost surely going to have relapses, so it's unwise to look for complete and permanent sobriety as the only proof of improvement. Just making an alcoholic stop drinking without further help is unwise. He drinks for a reason and if you deprive him without giving him something meaningful, he may develop other symptoms, such as a deep suicidal depression, or another form of drug abuse.

With help, a few alcoholics can return to social drinking, but most alcoholics who want to be cured must give up alcohol completely. Just one drink can get these people out of control. However, the alcoholic's total adjustment to family life, school, and social and work relationships is more important than whether or not he is sober all the time.

The fact that drinking may be illegal at your age in

your state should be only one consideration in making up your mind about the role you want alcohol to play in your own life. Drinking carries with it great responsibilities — to yourself and to others.

Like anyone else, teenagers drink for good and bad reasons: to loosen up, forget personal troubles, express rebellious feelings toward adult authority, have a good time, fit in with the rest of the crowd, and feel more adult.

Many adults don't have the maturity to handle alcohol wisely. Will you?

6

THE SOUND OF
ONE HAND CLAPPING:
LSD AND OTHER
HALLUCINOGENS

During the Middle Ages, epidemics of a strange illness swept through Europe. It was called St. Anthony's Fire, after the saint at whose shrine victims prayed for relief. Afflicted people suddenly developed vomiting and cramping pain in the abdomen. The tips of their noses and ears, or fingers and toes dropped off. Others couldn't sleep, saw horrifying visions of demons and monsters, and died from convulsions. In the seventeenth century, it was discovered that St. Anthony's Fire was caused by *ergot,* a fungus that grows on rye, as well as on wheat and other grasses. Unsuspecting eaters of bread made from infected rye fell ill with *ergotism,* the modern name for St. Anthony's Fire. Luckily, with proper control, the disease became very rare.

Ergot is a chemist's treasure chest, for it contains many substances called ergot alkaloids, which are responsible for the symptoms of ergotism. They also have important medical uses and high research value. So scientists are always trying to find new alkaloids in ergot, or change the known ones in the laboratory.

In 1938, Swiss researchers changed an ergot alkaloid and produced D-lysergic acid diethylamide, or LSD. At first, it didn't look like a particularly important drug, so it was put back on the shelf. Then, in 1943, one of the men who had made LSD started studying it again. During this work, he accidentally ate a tiny amount and had a weird emotional reaction that lasted several hours. He grew restless, dizzy, and experienced colorful visions and daydreams. He guessed that LSD was the cause and deliberately took another dose to prove he was right.

But even with these startling effects, LSD did not become well known right away. For a while, it was used only as a research tool to create an artificial state of insanity resembling the serious mental illness, schizophrenia.

Then, in the 1950's doctors cautiously began giving LSD treatments to patients with alcoholism, drug addiction, and many other problems. They reported fantastic success — at first.

More often than not, when a new drug is discovered it is acclaimed uncritically at first. LSD was no exception. Many of the early studies of LSD therapy were done poorly and unscientifically. At present,

LSD treatment of alcoholism, drug addiction, and criminal behavior is still highly controversial. LSD may have some promise in several areas. It is used in the psychiatric treatment of certain people who have trouble talking to their psychotherapist, loosening up, and remembering the events of the past. (It is used in minute doses before sessions.) The drug is also administered in certain cases of childhood schizophrenia (a severe emotional illness that hits children in their earliest years and is very difficult to reach by other methods). And, patients dying painfully of diseases like cancer have been given LSD. The drug seems to diminish physical suffering and fear of death.

Much more work will have to be done before it can be said for certain how valuable LSD really is in treating these conditions.

One of the best known scientists working with LSD was a brilliant young Harvard psychologist, Dr. Timothy Leary. From his work with emotionally troubled people, Dr. Leary grew convinced that LSD might give well-adjusted individuals the key to a deeper understanding of themselves and help them discover new ways to live in peace, harmony, and love. His idea was that through LSD and other psychedelic (meaning mind-influencing or mind-manifesting) or hallucinogenic drugs, a person could realize how unnecessary it was to claw his way to the top to get satisfaction out of life. All he had to do was relax, open up, and expand his awareness of the beauty in everything, most of all in himself. Soon Dr. Leary and his associates left Harvard, to become missionaries for their philosophy.

Many young people in the early 1960's were only too ready to listen to attractive leaders like Leary and to follow the well-known slogan: "Tune in, turn on, drop out." For years, sensitive young people had been getting more and more harrassed by a society that seemed to them to have abandoned any sense of values. So the gospel spread. Soon LSD and other psychedelics were being taken throughout the U.S.A., at first mostly on college campuses and in some artistic and intellectual circles.

Many young people actually dropped out, leaving comfortable homes and good schools to live, often in great poverty, in dilapidated parts of our large cities. Places like San Francisco's Haight-Ashbury district, or New York's East Village became famous for their strange new inhabitants.

Some of these people were called hippies, and although their original number was small, their impact upon American culture was great. The true hippies were the direct descendants of yesterday's beat generation of artists, poets, and rebels. Like many of the beats, they were not concerned with intellectual pursuits. They were more interested in the "direct experience of life," boosted by LSD, pot, and other psychedelics.

Dedicated hippies stressed simplicity, spontaneity, and sharing — of money, food, human warmth, sex. To "do your own thing" was what really counted.

THE SOUND OF ONE HAND CLAPPING:
LSD AND OTHER HALLUCINOGENS

The effects of the hippie style were felt especially in popular music, art, and fashion.

Adult response to the hippies was predictably strong, and mixed. As so often happens, what began with the young spread quickly to the adult world. Although there were really very few hippies following the simple, open life, their influence upon the adult consumer was strong. Yet many of the same adults who liked TV shows with psychedelic lighting and fashions put down the hippies themselves with disgust, and perhaps with a little jealousy too. They wrote them off as "dirty bums stoned on drugs," living without responsibility, and interested in nothing but pleasure.

Despite this disapproval, the movement grew. By the mid-1960's, the number of younger teenagers leaving home and migrating to the hippie districts swelled alarmingly, as did openly lawless elements like the motorcycle gangs. These people were not interested in exploring the mysteries of self. They just wanted kicks. And, all too often, *any* drug would do. They played Russian roulette with drugs, taking a pill, any pill, even if they didn't know what it was or where it came from.

Now that LSD was not being used just by a few bearded artists, the underworld quickly became involved in it. True, many makers and dealers were young people out to turn a quick buck. But increasingly, distributors of the psychedelics were adults connected with the same sprawling empire of crime that supports the world dope market.

It all added up to one conclusion: The peaceful vision of the hippies had turned into a tragic nightmare.

Pure LSD is a colorless, odorless, powder that dissolves easily. In drug slang, LSD is called *acid* or *sugar*. Taking a dose is dropping acid, taking a trip, or tripping. These days, it is usually delivered in tablets or capsules or as *dots* on pieces of paper; less often in sugar cubes. It also comes concealed on such unlikely exotic objects as postage stamps, chewing gum, hard candy, or soda crackers. A dose sells for about $2 to $10.00.

LSD is usually taken by mouth; occasionally, abusers administer it intravenously. The strength of LSD is unbelievable; it is one of the most potent drugs ever discovered. As little at 1/280 thousandths of an ounce can produce spectacular changes. The average trip is taken on a dose of one hundred to two hundred and fifty micrograms (*mikes* in abuser lingo). A microgram is *one millionth* of a gram. And *one ounce* could give a trip to about 250,000 heads.

Scientists have no clear explanation of LSD's action upon the nervous system. Very little acid seems to get to the brain. (After animals are given LSD, most is found elsewhere in the body, such as in the liver.)

Even more than any other drug on the scene, the response to LSD and the psychedelics appears to be strongly influenced by what's on a user's mind when he takes the drug, the place in which he trips, and the people he's with. Each person's reaction is unique; not everyone will experience the kinds of feelings recorded here. Most acid heads say their best experiences have been with friends who really dig each other, to the accompaniment of great music and fragrant incense. Of course, even with the best preparation, a user can still have a bad trip or *bummer,* on LSD — even with a friend or a *guru* (a person who believes he has reached a state of deep spiritual enlightenment, and who supposedly guides an LSD initiate on his way).

Within thirty minutes to an hour after taking LSD, the user's senses are powerfully affected, especially vision. Objects shift, bend, and flow into each other. Patterns of gorgeous color play across the wall and ceiling. Ordinary white light appears as pure and dazzling as a burning star, surrounded by rainbow halos.

The smell of a rose, the touch of velvet, the sound of a song bring delight. Soon the whole of the information being fed into the brain can not be separated from the parts. At first a painting may seem incredibly meaningful, but then its overall impact is lost as the tripper drowns in details (the bend of an elbow or the color of an eyelash). For a few, one kind of sensation is converted to another. Music is "felt," or sound is "seen." (This experience is called *synethesia.*)

Then deeper psychological changes occur. The body seems to change, sometimes enlarging or shrinking to frightening or amusing size. Emotions acquire a life of their own. You may be hurled up by a surge of joy one moment; the next, you plummet into black despair. Or there is a numbing icy fear, then a soothing by profound calm and peace. The tripper loves those around him and feels his identity merge with theirs. Then, suddenly, he is suspicious: Are they mocking him, making fun of his love? Will they turn on him now that he's helpless from the drug?

Past, present, and future grow tangled up. The tripper may feel he is a child again, reliving events from earliest years. These are sometimes reproduced faithfully, or happen as in a daydream. These recollections may give a feeling of contentment, or terror. Or he may feel that what he is experiencing right now is earth-shakingly important.

LSD is called an *hallucinogen,* a drug that makes the abuser hallucinate. However, seeing weird things that are not there isn't as common as is supposed. What the tripper experiences more often are distortions or misperceptions of objects that actually are around him. Flowers in a picture on the wall may seem to move or grow or change into faces.

Trippers can often think quite clearly while on LSD if they put their minds to it, but they just don't want to. Instead, thoughts fly from one idea to the next in no logical sequence. Everyday experiences may take on deep, mystical meanings. The tripper's name is called and this rocks him to the depths of his soul. His name is *he*! He never thought of it that way before! Most users can usually remind themselves that their visions, wild thoughts, and mystical

insights are related to acid, and their new ''awareness'' may appear naive to them when they come
down from the trip.

Regular users of LSD claim that there can be an
orderly progression in the trip, to ever deeper levels
of self-awareness without horror. But experts have
not yet found reliable evidence to confirm that LSD
will bring such a state of intense self-knowledge that
the tripper's life will be permanently changed for the
better afterwards. LSD may offer the illusion of
growth, but that is far from the real article. And,
instead of being orderly, the average trip often
strikes the experimenter as a succession of different
experiences crowding upon him without a feeling of
overall logic.

LSD can also have physical effects, but these are
not serious at the low doses usually taken. Commonly, there will be some nausea, chilliness, rapid
heartbeat, trembling, and sweating of the hands. The
pupils of the eye enlarge.

Throughout the LSD trip, consciousness is not lost.
The average trip lasts about eight to fourteen hours
depending on the dose taken. The tripper doesn't
sleep, and it is highly unlikely that he'll want to do
the things he customarily does when straight, like
working. After the main effects have worn off, it
may take a day or two more before he feels completely back together again.

What are the dangers associated with LSD? It
does not cause physical dependence or addiction.
There are no withdrawal symptoms associated with

stopping a trip. Psychological dependence does occur, but the emotional craving is quite mild, compared with the amphetamine head's need for pep pills. Tolerance develops quite rapidly, but only if repeated doses are taken close together. If the user trips weekly or so, he will get the full effect from the same amount of LSD each time. So, the difficulties with LSD are related to the trip itself, to what LSD does to the mind, on a short- or long-term basis.

PANIC — Do you remember how you felt the first time you went on a roller coaster? That scary feeling that you didn't have control of things — that they had control of you? And how you tried to hold on desperately, but felt as if you were going to be flung out of your seat?

Now imagine the same sensation, but a thousand times stronger! Some users on a trip actually feel their minds slipping away, and develop overwhelming panic.

Sometimes this panic can be calmed by a friend, or by remembering that LSD is causing the feeling. But sometimes panic is so deep that nothing helps. Victims have been found dashing wildly about and have had to be restrained from hurting themselves or others. Luckily, this extreme fearfulness usually leaves quickly, as the acid wears off.

DEPRESSION — On acid the user may hit rock bottom and stay there. Images of death, grief, and hopelessness torture the mind. If not watched carefully, the depressed tripper may try to kill himself. Like the panic state, serious depression usually disappears when the trip is over, but it may outlast the trip and continue.

PSYCHOSIS — This is the most common and worst bummer of all. The emotional reaction is hard to distinguish from a total nervous breakdown. Hallucinations are terrifying. Changes in the body's image are sickening.

Suspiciousness, outright delusions of being watched or followed may send the tripper on a mad escape or make him assault people, although violence is far less common with acid than with amphetamines and cocaine. Only a few homicides committed by people on LSD have been reported.

The "imitation" psychosis with LSD usually lasts only hours or days, but it can go on longer. And there are other disasters. A user can hurt or kill himself accidentally because he believes LSD has given him magic powers, such as the ability to fly. Auto accidents have occurred when a tripping driver has seen the white line bend and followed it to wind up in a ditch or in the opposite lane of traffic.

Aside from the size of the LSD dose, and where and with whom the LSD is taken, the most important causes of a bad trip are the basic personality of the tripper, and what is bothering him. If a user is feeling fine, he stands a better chance than if he's depressed, angry, or suffering from serious problems. Although anybody can have a bummer, how quickly and how well the pieces fall back in place depends to a large extent on how stable the person is to begin with. The tiniest dose of LSD can cause severe psychoses in sensitive people who have an underlying emotional disturbance. Acid, even more than alcohol, uncovers inner conflicts and pain that may have been suppressed.

If a trip is bad enough to require hospitalization, the victim is given heavy doses of tranquilizers like Thorazine® to combat his agitation, suspiciousness, and fear. (A sympathetic doctor may help some people on bad trips recover without hospitalization, simply by saying the right things to convey the feeling that they will be all right.)

Usually, the tripper returns to reality quickly, but there have been cases where a victim has continued to have psychotic symptoms even after medication and has had to spend months in the hospital. Psychotherapy is often given to help him understand the problems that made him have such a bad experience. Sometimes it is recommended that he continue seeing the doctor after he leaves the hospital.

In a study of people given LSD under good medical supervision, only one per cent had bad trips. But under unsupervised circumstances, using unknown amounts of LSD, which may be badly prepared, the number of bummers is bound to be much higher, although how high no one can say for sure. Correct statistics are hard to get because the friends of a user on a bummer may treat him with their own supply of Thorazine®, so that he never sees a doctor at all, or sees him so much later that his symptoms are not blamed on LSD.

Compared to the total number of LSD trips, the

percentage of bummers is probably small, but the tripper is taking a gamble every time he trips. And there are long-term emotional and physical hazards that are associated with LSD.

CHRONIC PSYCHIATRIC DISABILITY — Certain people, especially those already mentally disturbed, go on to suffer chronic disturbances after taking LSD, *with or without a bad trip.* Even with the best care, some don't fully recover after a bummer. Depressed users may never be able to shake off their feelings of dejection and despair. Persistent *paranoia* is a common type of post-LSD disorder. The victim stays suspicious, resentful, and mistrustful. He isolates himself from social contact because of his fear of harm. Frequently psychiatrists see a mixture of symptoms: depression, anxiety, disordered thinking, confusion. These mixed states may never entirely clear up, or else they seem "cured," only to reappear under stress.

The number of times LSD is taken may have no relationship to how mentally sick the user gets. Some users have taken thirty or more trips without being hospitalized or having a bummer. On the other hand, there are users who have had serious prolonged maladjustments after just one bad LSD experience.

PERSONALITY CHANGES — These are harder to define than spectacular symptoms like suicidal depressions or paranoia. A number of acid takers do change their basic attitude towards things, become much less interested in the usual life goals that society accepts as desirable, getting a college degree or a well-paid job, living a normal family life, etc. People who undergo such changes see them as improvements, and often become LSD crusaders, encouraging everyone to turn on. Although they may feel more creative and unchained, their lives often look disorganized and distinctly less productive than before. For all their talk about how acid made them more loving, it appears easier for them to generalize about loving everybody, than to get really close to one person.

Certainly, the majority of people who trip with LSD do not undergo such radical personality alterations. With the ones who do, it's very difficult to say how much the changes are due to LSD, and how much comes from the pressure of the underground social scene to conform to the current life style. It is also possible that those who develop personality changes would have done so sooner or later anyway because of other pressures in their lives.

FLASHBACKS — Even after good trips, a small number of users have spontaneous recurrences of a part of the LSD experience. These last for a few seconds or minutes, sometimes longer. *Flashbacks* occur during emotional stress. They may be triggered by music or bright lights, or just come from nowhere. They may persist for as long as two to three years after a trip, without the person ever taking LSD again. The same bright visions or hallucinations, or the feelings of panic, or suspicion, or wild happiness occur just as they did on a trip. Flashbacks occur unpredictably only about once a month or even less often, but a few unfortunate users have been bothered by them many times a day. Perhaps they are due to permanent brain damage, but this remains to be proven.

CHROMOSOMAL ABNORMALITIES — Since 1967, different researchers have discovered that adding LSD to normal human white blood cells in the test tube has produced changes in *chromosomes*. (Chromosomes are messengers of heredity found in every body cell, and they determine how the biological inheritance from each parent will be expressed in each child, for instance hair, skin, and eye color.) Researchers have also found that LSD users show chromosomal abnormalities in white cells taken directly from the body.

So doctors are worried that LSD, by permanently changing a drug user's chromosomes, might cause his children, or even the children of more distant generations, to be born dead or deformed. Yet another source of worry is that some of these abnormalities resemble changes seen in leukemia, cancer of the blood. The specter of that dread disease is related both for trippers and their children.

All this research has alarming implications, but it is controversial and seriously questioned by other scientists who have not always been able to repeat the original findings. The studies so far are based only on small samples of LSD users. LSD has not been around long enough, and this chromosomal effect has not been known about long enough for the doctors to say whether changes will be permanent or not. Other drugs, and illnesses caused by viruses, also change chromosomes, and later the chromosomes return to normal. Although laboratory animals given LSD early in pregnancy have delivered abnormal or stillborn babies, there is still, at this writing, only questionable evidence that any human mothers have borne damaged children because of LSD.

Until the matter can be settled for certain, LSD tripping may mean taking another gamble on the welfare of your future children, and you should consider this possibility. This especially holds true for young mothers already pregnant.

Bad trips, chronic emotional illness, and the possibility of damaged babies have made young people and adults alike think twice about acid. The law has played a large part in putting down LSD too, by imposing stiffer penalties for dealers and users (see Chapter 10). The LSD that is coming from underground laboratories these days is often impure, cut with other drugs, and so dangerous that the word has gotten around to stay away from it. Many young people stopped taking LSD because tripping had turned into a dead end for them. Instead, they converted to other ways of cultivating self-awarness and fulfilling themselves, such as spiritual meditation without drugs, and political or social activity.

For all these reasons, the LSD "happening," which reached such a peak in the mid-1960's, now appears to be leveling off. Some experts believe that LSD abuse will continue to decrease rapidly from now on, although there is still plenty of acid on the current scene.

OTHER HALLUCINOGENS

There are many other hallucinogens that vary in strength, origin, duration of action, availability, danger, and popularity, but they all give one kind of trip or another, and can all cause psychotic experiences if taken in high enough doses, or by people already disturbed. Some have come and gone rapidly, taken up in the restless chase after that elusive bigger high, only to be rejected in favor of something newer and "better." Others like marijuana, have been constantly on the scene.

Heads are not just looking for a bigger thrill; they want a drug that is cheap, easily concealed or so widely found in the world around us that the law will have a hard time controlling it.

Some of the hallucinogens described in the chart on pages 80–81 are obtained from nature, and were used in ancient religious ceremonies and primitive medicine long before they made the contemporary drug scene. Others are new ones produced in the laboratory. According to authorities, a different hallucinogenic drug appears on the underground market every month. Insofar as we now know, psychedelics, old and new, may cause some psychological dependence, but no physical dependence. Abusing or selling most of them for the purpose of abuse is generally prohibited under federal and state drug laws (see Chapter 10).

OTHER HALLUCINOGENS

DRUG	SOURCE	HISTORY
Belladonna alkaloids, including scopolamine, stramonium	Group of chemically related substances, widely distributed in plants throughout world	Used for generations in ritual and folk medicine. In modern medicine, sold over counter for relief of asthma and in nonprescription sleeping pills (occasionally abused for barbiturate-like down effect
DMT (Dimethyl-trptamine)	Found in seed or beans of various plants in West Indies, South America. Also made synthetically	Used for centuries in Haiti, Venezuela, Brazil, Colombia by Indians in rituals, orgies, war preparations
Mellow Yellow	Scrapings from dried banana skins	Half-jokingly, half-seriously used on drug scene during last few years
Mescaline	At first, chemically obtained from peyote; now made synthetically	
Morning Glory Seeds	**Heavenly Blue** or **Pearly Gates** varieties contain LSD or LSD-like drugs	Some popularity with druggies in past few years; cheaply, easily obtained at flower stores
Nutmeg	Common spice; psychoactive ingredient probably an oil called *myristicin*	In past, abused in prisons, occasionally abused on drug scene today
Peyote	Buds of small cactus of same name from northern Mexico, southwestern U.S.	Used for centuries by Mexican Indians. Came to U.S. after Civil War; used in rituals by Plains Indians. One of first hallucinogens to interest psychologists and artists in recent drug scene
Psilocybin, Psilocin	Found in certain Mexican mushrooms; also made synthetically	Used for thousands of years by South American Indians in rituals and for pleasure
STP (DOM) (4-Methyl-2, 5, Dimethoxy-amphetamine)	Made synthetically	Appeared in 1967 as "mystery" drug, purported to be biggest mind blaster of all. Supposedly named after motor oil additive, or for initials of "Serenity, Tranquility, Peace." Disappearing from drug scene, but still used in research.

DOSE AND TRIP	HOW SUPPLIED AND TAKEN	REMARKS
Variable Several hrs.	Stramonium leaves burnt; inhaled. Asthma "cigarettes" containing tobacco, belladonna alkaloids smoked. Various tablets swallowed	Physical effects from overdose severe (needs immediate medical care): dry mouth, hot, dry skin and rash, light sensitivity, blurred vision, enlarged pupils, thirst, vomiting, convulsions. Death: heart failure. Trip: may progress from pleasant sensations to confusion, restlessness, fear
60–150 mg. 45 min.–1 hr.	Ground into powder; eaten, sniffed. Synthetic sniffed, smoked: mixed with marijuana, tobacco, or taken intravenously	In high dose possible brain damage, convulsions. Trip: known for intensity, shortness
———— ————	Smoked in pipe or with tobacco.	Analysis shows no psychoactive ingredient, so any high is imaginary
300–500 mg. 4–12 hrs.	Powder taken straight or in capsule. Liquid taken by mouth or intravenously	Physical effects same as peyote; often less pronounced or absent. Trip: similar to peyote effects
As high as 200–300 seeds 4–8 hrs.	Chewed. Brewed into tea. Rarely taken intravenously	Physical effects may be severe: nausea, vomiting, chills. Death: shock, heart failure. Abuse not widespread
About a teaspoonful Several hrs.	Taken orally	Physical effects often severe: dry mouth, fever, thirst, flushed face; abuser very ill. Abuse limited: other hallucinogens give better trip
Variable; depends on strength of preparation 4–11 hrs.	Sliced, shredded, dried; eaten brewed into tea. Ground into powder; taken in capsules. Reduced to liquid; taken with coffee, milk, etc. Rarely taken intravenously	Physical effects usually not severe: increased salivation, flushed face, nausea, vomiting. Trip: colorful visual effects. Popular since decline of LSD. Legal for Native American Church to use for spiritual enlightenment
4–8 mg. (as powder) 4–6 hrs.	Mushrooms eaten. Synthetic taken orally, or dissolved, and taken intravenously	Physical effects usually not significant. Trip: especially strong visual effects
1–3 mg. or more 8–10 hrs. (Heads claim as long as 3 days)	Tablets and capsules taken orally, or dissolved, and taken intravenously	Physical effects not usually significant. Bad trip: treated safely with Thorazine®; this treatment dangerous if STP is not DOM but a mixture of unknown ingredients; it may be hard to tell "brand" of STP taken

7

POT LUCK:
MARIJUANA

"It's safer than all the martinis *you* drink! Why shouldn't I smoke?"

"Because you'll get violent or turn into a criminal! Because once you get a taste you'll want to try something stronger!"

"That's crazy. It makes you relaxed, that's all. You appreciate things more when you're high. I know someone who writes better poetry when he's stoned!"

"And what does he do when he's on a marijuana jag and not writing poetry? You'll only ruin your health and your mind!"

"Nobody ever got hurt from smoking grass. That's just a fairy tale you tell us because you don't know any better, or maybe you're jealous! What

right do you have to lecture me if you've never
turned on?''

*"I don't have to get cancer to know that it's
deadly! What if you get caught, how do you think
that would make us feel?"*

"It's not my fault if a lot of old squares make
stupid laws. What I do is my business, as long as I
don't hurt anybody!"

*What about hurting us? Your mother and I didn't
raise kids to watch them throw away life just for a
few kicks. We went through the same thing when we
were your age — we know what it's all about!"*

"If you really knew, you'd be smoking too!"

No other drug stirs up the arguments between
adult and teenager, parent and child, that marijuana
does. As this is written, all the facts about marijuana
are not on record. But let's at least find out what
actually is, and is not, known.

Marijuana is a mixture of the dried leaves and
flowering tops of *cannabis sativa,* a tall, leafy plant
that grows wild and is also cultivated carefully
throughout the world.

Dr. Helen Nowlis, a noted drug expert, states that
a great deal of confusion over the harmful effects of
marijuana comes from ignorance about cannabis.
She says that there are many different preparations
from this plant, but that they are often incorrectly
lumped together as just plain pot. (*Pot,* drug slang
for marijuana, is also known as *grass, weed, tea,
dope, stuff, mary jane,* and *boo.*)

Cannabis sativa is either male or female, but the unfertilized female plant is the most psychoactive. The psychoactive material is concentrated in the flowering tops and top leaves as a sticky resin, or gum. The amount of psychoactive material in a plant depends on the soil and climate, and also upon when and how it is harvested.

Cannabis resin is drawn off the top of the female plant just before it flowers and is turned into a product called *charas* in India, or *hashish* in the Mid-East and North Africa (*hash* to the American abuser). Weaker Indian mixtures consist of dried leaves, flowering shoots, and resin from the lower leaves, and are called *bhang* or *ganja*. American marijuana usually consists of dried, chopped leaves and flowering tops with their stems and seeds.

As far as strength is concerned, the aristocrats of cannabis are hashish and charas, while the least potent form is marijuana. Bhang and ganja are somewhere in between these two. So what we usually get in this country is a pretty inferior brand.

Chinese physicians prescribed cannabis for pain thousands of years ago, while in India folk doctors have used it for centuries. The followers of some Eastern religions took cannabis to expand consciousness and increase spiritual enlightenment — and still do. But it has no place in modern Western medicine at this time.

In popularity, cannabis is second only to alcohol across the world as an intoxicating, pleasure-giving agent. It's estimated that there are more than two hundred million regular cannabis takers, and that at least five to twenty million Americans have either sampled marijuana or use it regularly. Marijuana arrests, a rough index of pot popularity, have at least doubled in the past five to ten years.

In the Middle East, India, and parts of North Africa, where the cannabis habit has long flourished, it is often as easy to get as alcohol is in the U.S.A. Most users in these countries take cannabis preparations in moderation and can handle the less potent ones without any particular difficulty. Unfortunately, as with alcohol, there have also been severe dependency problems, for which the strongest varieties, like charas or hashish, are blamed.

Cannabis did not achieve popularity in the U.S.A. until recenty. As marijuana, it was first brought into the United States after World War I by Mexican laborers, and was initially a drug of the poor. Then it reached the underworld and was identified in the public mind with crime — and heroin. Pot was smoked by some intellectuals and artists, especially jazz musicians, but it had such a bad image that it rarely went beyond these groups, and little basic research was accomplished. The few experiments carried out were often unreliable, involving people already addicted to drugs or imprisoned criminals, instead of normal individuals. And no one knew what the psychoactive ingredient in marijuana really was because cannabis contains an incredible number of complicated chemicals.

Then, in the past ten years, marijuana made the

big time, first on the youth drug scene, where it was
linked with young people who backed liberal political
causes, social protest, and the new morality. But
soon, these distinctions grew blurred as Americans
from other classes and backgrounds began tasting
pot. Stories about marijuana appeared in national
magazines, local newspapers, and on every major
TV network. It was condemned — or hailed — as
the drug of the sixties.

Through all the uproar, research continued to be
spotty, producing conflicting evidence that was used
— and *still* is being used — by both the pro- and
anti-marijuana factions. Then, several years ago,
scientists in Israel were able to isolate from hashish
a drug believed to be the major psychoactive ingredient of cannabis. It's one of a group of substances called *tetrahydrocannabinols,* or *THC.* Now
that THC has been discovered, proper investigations
into marijuana are just beginning.

Most marijuana gets into the U.S. across the
Mexican border. Smuggling is carried on by underworld operators, but also by ordinary citizens who
conceal pot in their shoes, clothing, or car tires.

The price of pot varies from one place to another,
depending on the scarcity of the drug and its
strength. Varieties of marijuana rich in THC, like
Acapulco Gold or *Panama Red* are highly prized
by heads and highly priced by distributors. Illicit
dealers currently pay about $120 per kilo (2.2
pounds) or $3.50 per ounce wholesale, and sell pot
retail for about $20 to $25 per ounce. An individual

marijuana cigarette costs from fifty cents to $1.00.

But most direct dealing is not carried on by big-time criminal operators. Instead, users themselves sell marijuana to finance their own habit. Other users are not even that interested in money and may turn a small profit or give the weed away to friends. But if a big shortage is on, the prices go sky high and heads hoard marijuana as if it were real gold.

Marijuana is usually smoked. Marijuana ciga-rettes are called sticks, reefers, or joints. Colorful stores known as "head shops" have sprung up in many large cities, and sell paper for hand-rolling, incense to cover the pungent, sweetish smell of pot, and other psychedelic paraphernalia, such as holders for "roaches" (the butt ends of joints, which contain a large amount of THC). Some solve the roach problem by rolling reefers with filters, which enable smokers to consume the weed down to the last puff.

Pot smoking has the appearance of some elaborate ritual. In a group, a single reefer is usually passed on from one person to the next. Smoke is inhaled deeply into the lungs and held in. Smokers actually learn to regulate the quickness and intensity of the high by the rate, depth, and length of inhalation.

Marijuana is also smoked in pipes, brewed into psychedelic tea, or put into food like cookies. Some-times it is cut with ordinary tobacco, or oregano, a kitchen spice. Hashish is either smoked or eaten in honey, candies, or cake. Some sophisticates coat it with opium, and smoke this mixture.

The effects of smoking marijuana begin almost

immediately as the smoke goes directly from the lungs into the bloodstream. They last from two to four hours. When a cannabis preparation is eaten, onset of action is from one half to one hour, and the high lasts a little longer.

Most smokers show a few reasonably mild physical changes. Pulse quickens, eyes redden, (though the pupils do not enlarge), mouth and throat feel dry and scratchy, and there may be a slight urge to urinate. Some people feel nauseated or have diarrhea. Others get hungry and crave sweets. Despite what you may have heard, there is no reliable evidence to show that marijuana or any cannabis preparation stimulates sex drive directly; but with inhibitions loosened, sex may seem more enjoyable.

There are no known lasting physical ill effects from smoking pot and so far no one has ever died from an overdose. There is controversial evidence from abroad, however, that prolonged abuse of strong cannabis in large amounts can damage your health.

In a study from India, thirty to forty per cent of heavy hashish users reported inflammation of the eyes (*conjunctivitis*), chronic inflammation of the lungs, and various digestive disturbances. Many also suffered from poor nutrition and a decline of general health. In the quantities most Americans smoke marijuana, it appears at the present time — and all the facts are not in yet — that as drugs go, it's not particularly dangerous to the body. But what about the dangers to emotional health?

Studies of marijuana's influence on the brain and the nervous system are incomplete. From what little is known, it exerts a complex combination of depression and excitement on the mind. The emotional impact of pot, like the psychedelics, is closely related to the personality and immediate situation of the smoker, and the conditions under which he takes the drug.

After smoking a joint, or after correspondingly small doses of THC, there is a feeling of dreamy relaxation. Thoughts float free and detached from everyday logic. Past memories may emerge with sharp clarity, or an event that happened an hour ago can not be recalled.

Sometimes the smoker gets happy, gay, and goofy. Or occasionally depression is the first mood that strikes; it may persist, especially if pot is combined with alcohol, but usually it changes into pleasure. And some people experience depression on coming down from being high.

Behavior is greatly influenced by whether the grass is smoked alone or with other people. Alone, there may be inactivity and even a little drowsiness. But for most people stoned in a group, gaiety and lots of talk prevail.

After smoking several joints, or stronger pot, or a higher dose of pure THC, time and space grow progressively more distorted. Minutes rush together, or are stretched out. Close objects retreat into the distance. As with LSD, the senses seem sharpened. Colors seem more colorful, music more meaningful.

The image of the body can change too. The smoker may feel light as a feather or heavy as lead. Thoughts grow more and more disconnected; mood changes become more unpredictable and intense.

People who are given very large amounts of THC, doses that match the strongest pot or hashish, report that all the effects mentioned increase substantially, but that sensations that were pleasant at smaller doses become *unpleasant* at the higher ones. In addition, there are vivid hallucinations, usually visual; illusions in which commonplace things are distorted; and *delusions:* weird, strange ideas.

These effects of THC or hashish closely resemble an acid trip or a peyote experience. American marijuana does not contain enough THC to blow most people's minds, if only one or two joints are taken. But if the person goes on to smoke really strong grass or hashish or a lot of weaker pot, the chances of having a bad experience, instead of just getting a little high, rise accordingly.

Pot does not seem to produce physical dependence, but frequent users can develop psychological dependence. It's debatable whether tolerance develops or not. Some regular smokers say they need more pot to get stoned; on the other hand, there are experienced users who seem to require less of the drug to get an effect.

A few users inevitably go from the experimental stage, or occasional use, to smoking marijuana continuously, using it to the exclusion of everything else — school, work, and even good social relationships. The pot head often is the same type of person as other drug abusers. He is someone who is immature, unable to stand up under stress, has a desire for immediate kicks, and lacks self-assertion in normal life tasks.

The number of pot heads is probably not large compared to the number of people in the U.S. who smoke marijuana without becoming seriously dependent. But, in places where people have been using cannabis regularly for years, getting severely involved with the drug happens frequently enough to make it a genuine public health menace.

You can have severe emotional reactions after smoking only one joint, if your personality is unstable to start with, or if, for unknown reasons, your nervous system is highly sensitive to cannabis.

Pot panic — terror that comes from feeling that your mind is slipping away from you — is the best-known bad experience. You may become severely depressed, as already described, or else lose touch with reality and become psychotic, as with LSD. Panic, depression, and psychosis from marijuana usually clear up rapidly. Very few people have the kind of bad trip that requires hospitalization. But this may be true only because the marijuana used by Americans is a much weaker psychedelic drug than LSD.

The story appears to be quite different in Eastern countries, where the strongest preparations of cannabis are heavily abused. Doctors in India and Morocco blame cannabis for a great deal of mental illness. Some Western experts question their findings, believing they are based on unscientific studies. However, there's no doubt, East or West, that THC-rich drugs, like hashish, can cause temporary psychosis. But reliable evidence about long-term harm to the mind is still lacking.

In the East, it is believed that a heavy cannabis habit frequently leads to poor social relationships and loss of meaningful life plans. Western opponents argue that the people who show these changes in motivation often come from disadvantaged, poverty-stricken backgrounds where nutritional, educational, and economic deprivation, *not* cannabis, have played the major role in rendering personalities ineffective.

There are also many in our country who blame marijuana for defects in character, disregarding the increasing numbers of "normal" Americans who are turning on with pot, apparently without changing for the worse. Pot is often identified with the whole hippie, radical scene. Some believe it's responsible for everything from laziness, lack of drive, and long hair, to campus riots and revolutionary activity. Whatever its real effects on body or mind may be, pot has become a rallying point in the battle between hip and square. Unfortunately, sometimes this only obscures the basic issues of what the drug really will or will not do.

Although research into personality change with marijuana has not been finished, the most educated guess is that the majority of those who smoke occasionally do not alter their life style for better or worse, any more than those who drink alcohol in moderation.

People do not magically become criminals, revolutionaries, or dropouts. And they do not become more creative either. Like other psychedelics, marijuana may make you *think* you are sensitive and creative. Although you may enjoy more, at the moment, what you see, hear, or feel, converting your pleasure into a meaningful artistic experience that others will enjoy is quite another matter.

Every psychiatrist who treats adolescents sees patients who smoke pot heavily. How much of their personality problems is due to marijuana, and how much to basic character? Unlike the stimulant pep pills, cannabis seems to encourage the passive side of your nature, making you look away from the outside and into the inner world, turn from the future to immediate kicks, and disregard any stresses that may be present in your life right now.

If you've put in a hard day working or studying, you might want that kind of release. But if you already have big problems, it is a definite possibility that your personality and marijuana will get along fine, but at some expense to your life plans.

Each of you is trying to establish how assertive to be, to discover what your talents and interests are and how to make the most of them. Who does not at times feel so helpless, or find the future so scary that fun and games in the present become much more tempting? This does not mean that everyone who tries pot is going to become a head.

But perhaps you can see why a drug like marijuana can hold such an attraction at just this particular time of life.

The tendency of marijuana to emphasize the passive side of things does not fit into the popular image of the drug as a cause of violent behavior. Drugs like cocaine and pep pills are the ones most responsible for aggressive outbursts, especially in people with criminal backgrounds. While assaults and even homicides have been perpetrated by people who are stoned on pot, these cases, at least in the U.S. and other Western countries, are rare.

Because cannabis preparations can throw off coordination and judgment to varying degrees, the performance of complicated physical tasks, such as driving, may suffer. While there is disagreement as to how badly small amounts of weak marijuana will affect a driver, smoking strong pot or hash is very likely to alter your decisions behind the wheel for the worse. Safety experts would rather see no one drive after taking even a small amount of alcohol. The same principle should hold true for pot.

Marijuana critics claim that pot leads to the abuse of stronger drugs, like heroin. Certainly, it is true that heroin addicts often give a history of having smoked marijuana.

But as with any drug, marijuana smoking, and what else it may lead to, is heavily influenced by social conditions. In the past, abuse flourished predominantly in the slums, where poverty, misery, and underground heroin traffic flourished too. There is always plenty of grass floating around for the children of poverty to sample, and if a person wants to make the big step to H, that is just fine with the crimelord. It means more money in his till. But even under these conditions, although the majority of heroin addicts may have sampled pot first, all ghetto users who take marijuana don't go on to become heroin addicts.

Marijuana does provide certain sensitive young people with an invitation into more extensive drug involvement, but what those drugs will be depends very much on the particular scene the person is involved in, and on what the "going thing" may be. For middle-class college students or hippies, it is still more likely to be LSD, mescaline, and amphetamines like Methedrine®, not heroin. It is estimated that ten to forty per cent of collegiate pot smokers go on to try LSD at least once. If you have the potential to dig drugs, it is possible you will use many of them, and pot will be *only one*. But it is not logical to assume that pot alone can turn a reasonably well-adjusted person into a dope fiend!

"If marijuana really doesn't do most of the horrible things attributed to it, what's all the fuss about? Pot doesn't sound worse than booze. As a matter of fact, it sounds better! Why not just legalize it and concentrate control efforts on really dangerous drugs?"

There certainly are other drugs, like barbiturates, amphetamines, tranquilizers, and alcohol whose abuse seems to present much more of a threat than marijuana. And some responsible adults *do* believe that marijuana should be legalized. But others feel that simply making one more drug like pot available indiscriminately to everyone — especially a drug we presently know so little about — is going to create more problems than it will solve.

Many of the laws under which marijuana offenses are prosecuted are still outdated and based on unscientific misconceptions. Marijuana violators are frequently dealt with under the same regulations that punish heroin abusers and pushers. The possessor of pot can be liable for a felony, and conviction carries an extremely stiff jail sentence.

Until the basic research about marijuana shows just how dangerous the various cannabis preparations really are, many experts, such as Dr. Donald Louria, believe that the wisest course would be to reduce the penalties for possession for a person's own use so that a small crime would be punished by a small sentence. At this writing, federal marijuana laws dealing with users are being revised so that people possessing marijuana will probably be charged with a misdemeanor instead of a felony and receive lighter penalties if convicted. (See Chapter 10.)

The effects of arrest upon a pot user's future can be disastrous. Even though judges tend to be lenient with a young person, a suspended conviction on the record can really cause trouble when it comes to finding a job, applying for a passport, and going into certain professions. He may have to register as an addict with law enforcement officials wherever he goes.

As opposed to the experts who would maintain penalties for marijuana possession and use, other authorities feel that marijuana should be legalized and that law enforcers, attorneys, researchers, and mental health professionals should stop devoting their efforts to stamping out the drug. Instead, they feel these authorities should be working together to solve such problems as what strength of marijuana should be allowed, or under what conditions and at what age people should be permitted to smoke.

To some, just recommending lighter penalties for marijuana offenders will seem scandalous, let alone legalizing marijuana. But perhaps anything short of total legalization looks square and hypocritical to young people. Perhaps you believe that everyone should be allowed to do his own thing in peace, as long as no one gets hurt. *Examine that qualification, and remember that not enough is known yet about pot to say for sure how much it will hurt you, especially if smoked repeatedly over a long period of time.*

Marijuana contains small amounts of THC, a drug that in high enough doses can cause just as strong a bad reaction as LSD. If you legalize pot, what about hashish, which has a much higher THC content and is known to be more powerful and hazardous? "O.K.," you say, "we'll allow only marijuana cigarettes, containing definite amounts of THC."

But even then, everyone is different. How do you know that everyone who smokes legal grass will be able to handle it? *You* might, but how about someone younger, or more impulsive, or less stable?

Men have always been attracted to drugs, and probably always will be. Some drugs are helpful — when used in moderation and for the right reasons. It may be one thing to take pot for simple pleasure, but it is a very different situation if the *only* way you can feel content or self-confident is by smoking marijuana.

8

RIDE A DEADLY HORSE: HEROIN AND OTHER NARCOTICS

If someone gave you an injection of heroin, you probably would not get high. You might feel drowsy, or develop the jitters, or even get sick and vomit. Most important, you probably would not be particularly interested in repeating the experience for it simply wouldn't have been that much fun. Something different happens to the potential heroin addict. Shortly after his first dose — within seconds, if he shoots it into a vein — he is flooded with a fantastic sense of well being. Some describe it as a warm, intensely pleasurable sensation, located in the pit of the stomach. It grows, peaks, and slowly disappears, leaving an intense craving for more of the same.

Heroin is the most infamous member of a group of substances originally called *opiates.* They are directly or indirectly derived from *opium,* a sticky, brownish gum obtained from the seed pods of vivid red poppies that bloom in Iran, Turkey, Mexico, Yugoslavia, India, and China (to name only a few places where the opium poppy is cultivated).

Knowledge of opium and its power reaches back to the dawn of recorded time. Originally, the poppy grew only in Asia Minor. From there, its fame, and its seeds, spread to Greece, where references to it are found in medical writings from three centuries before Christ. Arabian physicians prescribed it, and traders from Arabia brought it to the Orient. By the seventeenth century, opium was familiar to European doctors, some of whom eventually came to the United States. Only crude opium extract was available until the early nineteenth century, when *morphine* was chemically isolated from opium and quickly became one of the most medically beneficial drugs ever discovered.

The identification of other drugs in opium, such as *codeine,* followed. As technical skill increased, it first was possible to make new semi-synthetic opiates in the laboratory, including heroin and *hydromorphine,* (Dilaudid®). Finally, scientists produced totally synthetic drugs like *methadone,* (Dolophine®) and *meperidine* (Demerol®) with properties almost identical to the original opiates. These drugs are called *narcotics* because of the particular combination of relieving pain and calming mental anguish.

At the turn of the century, narcotic addiction was a terrible affliction amongst women, who became addicted to cheap, over-the-counter medications that contained opium. However, this led to stricter controls, and narcotic problems in this country declined for a while. But within the past thirty years, narcotic addiction has been increasing substantially, first among the underprivileged, but more recently spreading into the teenage drug scene everywhere.

In 1680, the famous English doctor, Thomas Sydenham, wrote: "Among the remedies which it has pleased Almighty God to give to man to relieve his sufferings, none is so universal and so efficacious as opium." These words are equally true of the opium derivatives used today.

It is not really understood how this marvelous pain-killing effect is produced, although narcotics do seem to slow down the activity of nerve cells in the spinal cord. Patients given morphine often state that they feel detached from their suffering. Morphine also soothes the anxiety of the pain-ridden, promoting deep, satisfying sleep. A few people will feel better not simply because their pain is gone, but because they also experience euphoria, a state of joyful happiness. It is this euphoric sensation that the addict seeks.

Because narcotics cause contraction of muscles in the intestines, they may be useful in treating diarrhea (opium itself, dissolved in alcohol, is prescribed for this purpose as *paregoric*). Codeine, a pain-killer not quite so powerful as morphine, stops severe coughing. These are only a few of the ways the versatile narcotics can help sick people. But every positive effect for the ill can become a source of misery for the addict.

Heroin, also known as *H, harry, horse, junk, dope, shmeck, smeck, smack,* and *scag,* is the aristocrat of narcotics for American addicts. Originally, it was heralded as being non-addictive, and a possible cure for the morphine habit! Unfortunately, it turned out to be as addictive as other narcotics, and addicts seemed to prefer it because it gave them a better and stronger high.

The few good scientific studies done do not prove heroin's "superiority" and it is believed by some experts that heroin is so much more widespread than other narcotics because underworld suppliers find it to be easily made and concealed, with the biggest margin of profit for them.

Heroin is totally illegal, and is not prescribed by physicians in this country, who use morphine and the synthetic narcotics instead.

Heroin comes as a whitish powder, usually heavily mixed or cut with milk sugar or quinine. Much American heroin is produced in, or smuggled into, Mexico and then taken over the Mexican-American border. A great deal also comes from places like Iran and Turkey, reaching the U.S. from various European ports.

Heroin is purchased from underworld sources and sold to the addict on the *street,* as the local drug scene is sometimes called, by a pusher who may be clean, but who quite often is an addict himself. Heroin is packaged in a glassine wrapper, called a *deck,* or *bag,* or in capsules, *caps.* The amount of heroin in a deck depends on how much sugar or other substances have been used to cut the drug. The bigger the cut, the more the profit. Because of extensive cutting, most addicts are probably taking a much smaller amount of heroin and actually have weaker habits than they think.

The addict takes heroin by sniffing up the powder (*snorting*), by injection, and (rarely) by swallowing. The tools with which the addict prepares and administers his shot are called *works.* They may be stolen or homemade medical equipment. The works usually consist of a spoon, on which the heroin is dissolved, using the heat of a match and a crude hypodermic (a needle attached to an eyedropper and rubber bulb). The solution of heroin is sucked up into the syringe and injected just beneath the skin (*skin-popping*) or directly into a vein (*mainlining*), which gives the biggest kick and leads to the quickest habit. Morphine (*M, monkey*) and the other synthetic narcotics are taken by pill or injection.

The veins at the bend of the elbow are preferred; once these become clotted up, any other vein is used, including those in the hands and feet.

Opium itself is either eaten or smoked, but is not widely favored by American addicts. However, the use of the opium pipe is well known in the Orient. The opium dens of Hong Kong are infamous even to this day.

THE ADDICT: LIFE AND HARD TIMES

When a beginner who gets a thrill from his first jolt of narcotic starts repeating injections, everything will be fine for a while, but he soon will discover that he needs increasingly larger doses to give him the same high. This is because he is growing tolerant. Then he finds that if he cannot get enough narcotic into his system, he develops the well-known signs of withdrawal. By this time, in addition to being tolerant and psychologically dependent, he is hooked, or physically dependent.

This "breaking-in" process varies from one addict to another, but doctors believe he can become physically dependent upon narcotics after as little as two weeks of serious use. How much he will need after that to maintain a daily habit also varies, but it is not unusual for a heroin addict to require several shots or more at a cost of $20 or up, per day. Some addicts continue to get the same pleasurable high time after time; others find that they feel progressively less kick and wind up taking drugs only to prevent withdrawal symptoms.

The popular image of the heroin addict as a degenerate criminal, wallowing in degradation, physical illness, and moral squalor is not always true. A user conceivably could remain in reasonably good shape as long as he is on the drug. Disease, crime, and the descent down the social ladder are not consequences of the effect of the narcotic on the brain, but stem from the sacrifice of money, status, and self-respect in order to get a regular fix.

RIDE A DEADLY HORSE:
HEROIN AND OTHER NARCOTICS

Since narcotics are obtained illegally, the cost is likely to be high.

If the addict doesn't have the money to support his habit, or a readily available drug source (as do physician addicts), his life undergoes a gradual change for the worse, as the usual daily concerns of job, friends, school, marriage become subordinated to finding drugs. Eventually, he drops out of society, to exist in a shadowy junky world, where his worth is defined by his ability to score regularly without getting caught. And, for someone poor who can't get work, the life of an addict may seem more exciting and "busy" than sitting around doing nothing!

Most who become hooked have to commit crimes to get the money they need. Men steal; women prostitute themselves. While it was once believed that heroin addicts were not particularly dangerous, and that their offenses were usually directed against property rather than person, in recent years a rising tide of armed robberies, assaults, and even murders have been traced to junkies trying to put enough cash together for a fix. Heroin addicts are considered responsible for a large share of crime in our cities today.

A totally false idea about addicts is that they are sex-crazed. The opposite is true: heroin, if it does anything to the sex drive, decreases it. The pleasure of being high actually seems to become a substitute for sexual satisfaction. Indeed, it is in the nature of addiction for many heroin heads that they no longer need to cope with problems in achieving the usual life goals: raising a family, relating to the opposite sex, working at a satisfying job. Instead they greatly simplify living by searching for only one goal — chemical peace.

Addicts fall victim to a vast assortment of physical woes. Some are merely annoying; others can be fatal. Narcotic abusers are chronically constipated, because of heroin's spastic effect. Since the ability to recognize pain is decreased, the addict may cut, burn, or bruise himself without realizing that he is injured. The inability to cough properly, combined with poor nutrition, makes him a sitting duck for pneumonia.

Shooting up with unsterilized needles often leads to skin infection at the injection point. Germs can be directly introduced into the bloodstream, overwhelming the body's defenses, and lead to total collapse and death. Blood-borne infection can settle in any organ, and may seriously damage tissue. For instance, if infection reaches the heart, the delicate valves that control the rate and direction of blood flow may be destroyed, and the addict develops heart failure. A dangerous inflammation of the liver called *infectious hepatitis* is caused by a virus, and can be spread from one addict to another by sharing contaminated needles. Finally, many addicts live in a state of chronic malnutrition and serious vitamin deficiency, partly because narcotics suppress hunger, partly because money that should be spent on food goes for drugs instead.

The female addict is exposed to all these dangers,

plus two more. If she goes into prostitution, and most do, she may contract venereal diseases like syphilis or gonorrhea; if she becomes pregnant, her infant may be born physically dependent on heroin, and will have to be weaned from the drug.

Probably the deadliest threat to the narcotic addict is the overdose, or *OD*. Almost every day in our largest cities, young people are found dead, killed by OD, and abandoned by their frightened friends. These fatalities stem from the administration of an enormous dose of heroin, with the hopes of achieving a spectacular high. Or the addict who's used to weak heroin may change his source of supply and overdose himself on what he mistakenly believes is the same heavily cut dose he was taking before. Death by OD can also come from an unaccustomed combination of drugs, such as heroin and cocaine, or other dangerous substances used to dilute or cut the heroin, such as strychnine.

In high or unaccustomed amounts, heroin causes severe depression of breathing, oxygen starvation of the brain and coma. Prompt medical treatment is urgently needed, but since the addict feels terrified of capture, he usually employs makeshift methods to snap his stricken friend out of an OD, with tragic consequences.

Every addict is terrified of a drug panic too, when supplies of narcotics are dried up by police raids. Without heroin, he falls back on cough syrup containing codeine, paregoric, or other less satisfying drugs with some narcotic-like properties, such as tranquilizers, barbiturates, alcohol, and even aspirin. It is then one sees just how pitiful the addict's situation can be. There is little thought of getting high or happy. All he wants is something, anything, that will stop the pain of withdrawal.

So the addict's world is filled with fear. Fear that he won't find the drugs he needs, or the money to purchase them; fear of illness and overdose; fear of other addicts who prey upon him, beat him up, rob him of his precious fix, maybe even kill him.

What made the heroin addict the way he is? There is no one answer to this question, only many guesses:

The greatest number of addicts still, at this time, come from poverty-ridden backgrounds, where hope for a reasonable life, with educational, recreational, and vocational opportunities are denied from childhood. The victim, faced with day after day of grinding misery, menial back-breaking labor, or the perpetual boredom of unemployment, is easily tempted by the illusory happiness of drugs to escape from harsh reality. For some, the identity of being a wheeler-dealer addict pursuing a fix is preferable to being an unemployed useless wreck. The disadvantaged child growing up in the slums learns about narcotics almost as soon as he can walk. There are pushers in the streets and near the schoolyard, and they peddle everything. Often, before he touches heroin, he has been initiated into the drug scene by experience with glue sniffing, barbiturates, pep pills, or marijuana.

RIDE A DEADLY HORSE:
HEROIN AND OTHER NARCOTICS

Not every suffering slum child becomes an addict, so there must be other factors besides social disadvantage that create addiction. In the last few years, the use of hard narcotics has been spreading with bewildering speed among young people from many different social groups, not just the poor. Narcotic addiction is now regularly reported both in small Midwestern towns and Eastern suburban communities, where teenagers from middle-class and even wealthy families have fallen victim to the ravages of heroin. And they tell us that their pushers are not adults, but other kids.

Experts disagree over the explanation for what may turn out to be an epidemic of heroin experimentation among teenagers and young adults in the U.S. Perhaps they were just experimenting to start, trying to join the in-crowd, and then got caught up to the point where they could not stop. Perhaps youngsters from backgrounds with more financial advantages have been smothered with material goods, but have never received real emotional support and warmth, or have not been given any consistent set of values by their elders. Perhaps they are bored, easily persuaded to seek out newer, more dangerous kicks.

Psychiatrists believe that most addicts are not crazy. Their behavior is not bizarre or eccentric, and they are in touch with reality. However, regardless of social background, many are immature, easily-frustrated people, with a tendency to collapse into helplessness under routine stress.

But others, especially from poverty-stricken areas, don't fit this conventional image at all. They are energetic hustlers, endlessly on the move, manipulating people around them, gaining prestige and self-respect from their ability to score and evade the law.

Some experts believe that even a reasonably normal person can be turned into an addict when a physician administers too much narcotic over too long a period of time. But others feel that while *anyone* can be made physically dependent on heroin, you must have an underlying personality disturbance to grow psychologically dependent as well, and remain hooked.

The accessibility of narcotics plays a great role in the high addiction rates of doctors, nurses, and other people in the health fields. The addicted doctor may practice for years without anyone being the wiser, again disproving the myth that narcotic misuse automatically leads to personal degradation.

Whatever the first causes of addiction, heroin users are never quite the same as they were before they developed physical and psychic dependence. Even when the addict is withdrawn completely from narcotics, a strong unconscious link has apparently been forged between the relief of anxiety and narcotics, so that it is always easier for him to succumb to temptation again.

The attitude about drugs expressed by the society you live in plays a part in determining how addiction is created, tolerated, treated, and prosecuted. In the Far East, an extremely lenient and permissive view of drug use has prevailed until very recently. Opium was smoked for social purposes by members of the Chinese upper classes, and eaten in India with tea, over pleasant conversation. These social opium ceremonies did not lead frequently to serious dependence for the higher classes, but terrible problems with addiction exist for the lower classes in these same countries. In the West, especially in the U.S., instead of lenience and permissiveness, the pendulum has swung in the other direction, so that the addict may be severely prosecuted by the law, and often is viewed with unreasonable fear, hatred, and contempt.

Although the number of confirmed narcotic addicts in this country is not so large as our alcoholic population (several hundred thousand versus five to ten million), heroin abuse constitutes a major public health problem, and is definitely on the rise. Totally reliable statistics are not available yet. Narcotic addiction strikes young people in their teens and twenties, at a time when they should be most productive. While some evidence exists that addicts may go off drugs spontaneously in their late thirties or forties, many do not live that long, or spend a good part of their most useful years behind bars, or submerged in the drug culture.

TREATMENT FOR THE ADDICT

Nowhere is the difference between medical opinion and society's dictates more obvious than in the treatment of the narcotic addict. Although he is considered a sick individual by doctors, he is still likely to be imprisoned if he is caught with drugs. How effective can rehabilitation be in confinement, or with the threat of prison always in the background?

So far, no simple, reliable form of therapy has been found for the heroin addict, but many promising approaches have been developed.

The simplest way to break the habit is just to stop taking the drug. Abruptly depriving the addict of narcotics, (the *cold turkey* treatment) is still practiced in some jails and detention centers, and occasionally an unconfined addict will use this method on his own. He may be trying to cure himself. Or he may be taking the cold turkey route in order to start again with a new heroin dose that is small, cheap, and will give him the kick that tolerance now prevents him from obtaining.

The first changes after stopping dead occur around the time the addict would take his next dose, when he starts to feel anxious and irritable. About eight hours after his last shot, he often falls into a deep short sleep. When he awakens, physical symptoms begin, usually fifteen to twenty hours after his last dose, reach a peak in two or three days, and are usually gone in about two weeks.

Withdrawal symptoms are weeping, yawning, sneezing, sweating, loss of appetite, trembling, weakness, fever, nausea, vomiting, diarrhea, and chills. The phrase ''cold turkey'' comes from the plucked chicken appearance of the addict's skin. Cramps, back pain, headache and double vision may occur. Addicts can become completely delirious. Luckily, physical collapse and death are rare.

The routine medical management of heroin addiction consists of gradual withdrawal from drugs, using decreasing doses of narcotics. Methadone is usually used. Methadone causes much less severe withdrawal symptoms than heroin. During withdrawal, the patient's physical welfare is bolstered by proper diet, fluids, vitamins, and the occasional use of tranquilizers or sedatives to combat the jitters. Once off narcotics, the addict is given psychiatric and vocational guidance, and then hopefully is ready to face life again. Total physical recovery may take as long as six months, but the craving for drugs may never completely disappear.

The withdrawal therapy is usually undertaken in a hospital, away from the addict's unhealthy environment. The best known, largest public institutions for voluntary and involuntary treatment are the U.S. Public Health Service Hospitals at Lexington, Kentucky, and Fort Worth, Texas. Statistics from these hospitals have been discouraging. Many voluntary patients leave before rehabilitation is completed, and of those who do stay, and then return to the same oppressive social conditions, less than ten per cent remain off narcotics.

The standard office medical and psychiatric treatment of the addict is unrewarding. It is almost impossible to withdraw the average addict when he is on the street. Without adequate supervision or control, he is unreliable about maintaining himself, keeping appointments or taking medication.

The British have dealt with their narcotic problem by making drugs available through licensed hospital clinics, which dispense narcotics on a regular basis to registered addicts. Although the number of known addicts in England is far less than in the U.S., it has climbed in the past few years, and the British method has been seriously questioned. It is said that there are many unregistered addicts who prefer to get their heroin or morphine from illegal sources, because they can take as much as their finances will allow (physicians don't encourage increasing the dosage legally given). And some addicts claim that illegal heroin somehow gives a better high than the legally dispensed variety!

A promising new experimental program treats the addict as someone who needs a basic amount of drug in his system to function, much like the diabetic who has to receive insulin. Instead of heroin or morphine, however, the addict is given a daily oral dose of methadone, which does not produce an intense high like the one heroin supposedly gives. What is most important, tolerance to maintenance doses of methadone blocks out the euphoric effect of heroin, if taken while already on methadone. Without a desire for heroin, the addict is free to lead a normal life, and with proper guidance a very high rehabilitation rate has been achieved. But the addict must face the possibility that he will never be able to give up methadone, itself an addictive drug, although so far no serious physical effects have been reported from long-term use.

Another important new treatment was developed by Synanon, a group of "cured" addicts, and has been modified in places such as Daytop Village. Basically, the addict lives in a house or apartment with other addicts, his daily activities vigorously supervised by people who have already gone through the program. His contact with the outside world is very restricted at first. The use of drugs to ease withdrawal is frowned upon. Group techniques such as *attack* or *encounter therapy* examine the addict's defenses, including all the excuses he gives himself, in the presence of others like him, honestly and often mercilessly. The addict stays in this kind of program for several years, and may go on to make it his life's work. Synanon's success record is very high, but as in the methadone program, the applicants are screened carefully and are usually much better motivated than the average street addict.

The teenage addict has always had a particularly hard time getting assistance, even when he has desperately wanted it. Recently, a few pioneering organizations have been founded such as Encounter, and New York's Phoenix and Odyssey houses (see Page 149 for addresses) to treat teenagers who are already seriously addicted. And, in the case of one Encounter program, the aim is also to reach troubled young people who are not yet addicts, but who are in danger of becoming involved with drugs. These groups do great work, but they are short of funds, and cannot begin to meet the tremendous need for help.

Both New York and California have pioneeri: g and controversial programs for drug addicts. It is not the methods that are argued about, but the fact that addicts who have not robbed or assaulted may be committed to these centers against their will, treated, and followed closely after release on parole status. Lawyers argue that such a commitment violates civil rights, while some physicians believe that no addict will give up his habit under this sort of compulsion. (For a further discussion of heroin, narcotics, and the law, see Chapter 10.)

Other experts believe that involuntary commitment does help the addict by forcing him to be treated. Once established in the program, he is supposed to soak up the outside restraints on his self-destructive behavior, and with these restraints now a part of him, hopefully he is better able to control the drug craving.

There are still more questions than answers in connection with narcotics addiction, and especially teenage narcotic experimentation. Certainly, new treatment techniques are needed for the poorly motivated addict who is not really sure he wants to go off his drug. And, certainly, careful study of the many methods already developed is necessary to see which will stand the test of research and time. Each addict must be guaranteed the delivery of help which is best suited to his own particular hangups. Until very recently, afflicted teenagers who really wanted to kick heroin definitely have been shortchanged.

But even if every addict in the country received highly individualized care, it is unlikely that our narcotic dilemma would automatically be solved. As you have seen, experts are now looking beyond the private suffering of the young addict, beyond his troubled inner world, to the broad social forces in the outside world that create the breeding grounds for narcotic abuse.

Poverty is one such major force, but no longer can it be considered the *only* one, as shown by the recent spread of narcotic abuse throughout all levels of our society. A tremendous amount of time, effort, and money will be needed to investigate these forces in order to identify, control, and change them. But unless we are willing to make this kind of effort, and to make it right now, our present narcotic problem may turn into an even more overwhelming disaster, bringing tragedy into thousands of young and promising lives.

9

SNOW JOB:
COCAINE

Life is hard for the Indians living in the Andes Mountains of South America. Food is short and work is long and monotonous. For centuries these poor people of Chile, Peru, and Bolivia have chewed the leaf of the coca bush to raise their spirits and ease the pangs of hunger. Coca is often confused with cacao, the name of the tree whose beans provide us with chocolate and cocoa. The cocoa bush, cacao tree, and cola tree, which provides cola nuts and leaves for cola drinks, are not related to each other. The Indians actually are taking a drug called cocaine. The amount they get from chewing coca leaves is only mildly stimulating and moderately habit forming. However, extracted and purified, cocaine is a powerful stimulant that, when abused heavily, produces terrible effects on the mind and personality. In chemical form, cocaine (drug slang: *snow, coke,* or *snuff*) is an odorless, easily-dissolved white powder, with a bitter taste. At the turn of the century, doctors believed that cocaine would be the cure for morphine addiction. But, like heroin, which was once given for the same purpose, the cure usually turned out to be worse than the disease. The unfortunate victims often ended up more dependent on cocaine than they had ever been on morphine.

In the nineteenth century, the drug came into style among artists and intellectuals. One of the most famous "abusers" was Sherlock Holmes, the fictional detective-hero created by Sir Arthur Conan Doyle, a physician who surely knew of the pains and pleasures of cocaine. Holmes took cocaine to increase his famous powers of concentration or to relieve the depression and boredom that nagged him when he was between cases.

/ The only legitimate medical use of cocaine is as a local anesthetic. When a solution of the drug is applied to the eye or the throat, numbness develops rapidly so that minor surgical operations can be performed without pain. However, newer and more effective local anesthetics, like Novocaine® and Xylocaine® have been created through modern research so that cocaine is not employed very much for this purpose.

/ Cocaine is sniffed, or injected under the skin or directly into the bloodstream intravenously. On the drug breathing, heart rate, blood pressure, and temperature rise. The pupils of the eyes enlarge. There is a tremendous rise of good feeling, an incredible surge of power and joy. Fatigue vanishes, the abuser feels stronger, and the sex drive often increases. A person flying high on snow is overtalkative and restless. But when the stimulating effects wear off, they leave in their wake a striking sensation of fatigue and depression, which often leads the abuser to seek another shot promptly.

Sometimes the strength of the cocaine excitement becomes so unbearable that the abuser must take a depressant drug, like a barbiturate, either with cocaine or afterward, to cut down on the excitement. (A *speedball,* a combination of heroine and cocaine, is often taken by addicts for this purpose.)

Cocaine depresses the appetite and leads to nausea and other digestive disorders. Weight loss may be so great that the abuser has a skin-and-bone appearance. Shaking of the hands and epileptic seizures have been reported in those with heavy habits. As with other mainlining, skin infections and hepatitis may develop when cocaine is injected intravenously with dirty needles.

Cocaine makes the small blood vessels constrict or clamp shut, cutting down the flow of blood and oxygen supplied to the tissues by these tiny arteries. Because of this effect, abusers who sniff cocaine repeatedly get sores and ulcers of the nose. And those who inject themselves over and over again with cocaine in the same spot develop severe skin ulcers.

If the personality of the abuser is unstable enough,

the reaction to cocaine may be startling! (As always, dosage and the setting in which the drug is taken also play a part.) The individual becomes fearful and terror-stricken. Much like the amphetamine head, the coke head often grows paranoid, or highly suspicious and resentful. He believes that people are saying bad things about him behind his back, are persecuting him, are out to harm, and even kill, him. Responding to these wild ideas as if they were true, cocaine abusers have been known to attack and kill their imaginary persecutors. The belief that all drug users are aggressive, degenerate fiends stems mainly from the violent acts committed by people under the influence of cocaine and other stimulants.

Cocaine often causes hallucinations, which may be pleasant or frightening, or both. Cocaine also causes *tactile hallucinations;* the abuser feels things touching him that aren't there. This particularly unpleasant sensation of something crawling over the skin is also called *formication.* The effect is quite unusual for drugs, although alcoholics withdrawing from liquor do occasionally develop the same symptom. The sleeplessness associated with high doses of cocaine helps to increase the breakdown of personality. In the withdrawal state, hallucinations and depressions accompanied by suicidal activity may occur.

Unlike heroin, cocaine does not lead to physical dependence, and there is only a mild degree of tolerance. However, psychological dependence can be remarkably strong.

When painful emotional effects occur, they usually wear off rapidly as cocaine disappears from the body. However, both the chronic abuse of cocaine and the sudden withdrawal of cocaine, once one is heavily dependent upon it, can cause severe, and sometimes lasting, emotional illness.

As with heroin, an overdose of cocaine can kill. The coke head who has taken an OD rapidly grows extremely excited, with headache, high temperature, vomiting, abnormal pain, seizures, and loss of consciousness. He may recover, but in some instances dies in minutes. The heart and lungs literally collapse from the tremendous shock of the stimulant.

Although, medically, cocaine is not a narcotic, cocaine abuse nevertheless is dealt with under the same federal and state narcotic laws that apply to heroin and other narcotics. Legal penalties are very heavy in this country (see Chapter 10), and international control measures are also quite strict.

Chronic cocaine dependence doesn't present as much of a problem in America today among adults or teenagers as the abuse of other drugs. It seems to take rather specialized tastes to develop a head for cocaine. Cocaine is also quite expensive on the illegal market and not nearly so easy to get as the amphetamines, which give most of the same effects as cocaine.

Still, a lot of cocaine floats around the drug scene today. Many young people are experimenting with coke — more to get kicks than to explore the mystery of life. Most tasters don't get burned, but they are lucky, for cocaine is as potentially harmful as a loaded gun with the safety catch off.

10

DRUGS, CRIME, AND THE LAW

With all the outcry surrounding the drug issue to-day, one thing is certain: the moment you sell, use, or possess most psychoactive drugs without a prescription from a reputable practitioner, you are breaking the law.

Since 1914, the United States Congress has passed more than 50 laws to control drug abuse. Until very recently, this mass of federal legislation was often contradictory: some laws were based on modern information, others stemmed from old drug myths. For instance, although marijuana is not a narcotic, pot offenders in the past were dealt with under the same federal laws that punished heroin addicts and pushers.

Congress finally cut through the confusion by passing the Comprehensive Drug Abuse Prevention and Control Act of 1970. This act reorganizes many previous laws, using the latest information. Controlled psychoactive drugs now are classified according to their abuse hazards as well as their psychological and physical effects. And penalties of federal courts will now be based logically on the *kind of drug* as well as on the *type of offense* involved. The penalty for simple possession with no intent to push has been reduced, so that the days when a person could be sent to a federal prison for years just because he had a small amount of marijuana are over.

The new law sets up procedures for evaluating and controlling new psychoactive drugs; establishes drug quota systems for import, export, and domestic production; and strengthens the regulations governing the handling of records and prescriptions by doctors, other licensed practitioners, and pharmacies. Guidelines are set up for co-operation between federal, state, and local agencies, and a controversial "no-knock" section has been included, allowing federal enforcers to enter a place without warning when there is suspected drug dealing or use going on.

With the exception of alcohol, controlled drugs are grouped together (much as in this book) into categories or "schedules" (the legal term) of: narcotics or opiates; hallucinogens (including marijuana); sedative-depressants; certain minor tranquilizers; stimulants; and some medications that contain small amounts of narcotics with mild abuse potential.

The new law almost completely eliminates all

"mandatory" minimum sentences; thus, no longer does conviction for a drug offense automatically mean imprisonment or fine. Illegal simple possession is reduced from a felony to the less serious charge of a misdemeanor.

If it is a first-possession offense, the offender may be placed on a year's probation; if he sticks to the terms of probation, which may include treatment, all proceedings against him can be dropped without declaring him guilty. If a person is 21 or below when arrested for simple possession, and follows the terms of probation, he may eventually obtain a court order requesting erasure of all court records related to his arrest, trial, and probation — although a special non-public record may still be kept at the Justice Department to be referred to if he is arrested again. Once having completed the above procedure, the ex-offender is legally entitled not to mention the previous arrest when applying for a job, various licenses, etc.

The law deals most strictly with those who deal in drugs for high profit. Anyone who manufactures, distributes, or possesses with the purpose of manufacture or distribution is severely prosecuted according to the type of drug made or sold, and the violator's previous drug convictions. The penalty for first offenders when narcotics are involved is up to 15 years in prison, and/or fines of as high as $25,000; if there have been previous offenses, the penalty is doubled. Penalties for dealing in non-narcotic drugs are set lower. Conviction for illegal manufacture and dealing in cocaine, amphetamines, barbiturates, some nonbarbiturate sedatives, or psychedelics like LSD, marijuana, and mescaline, carries a maximum of five years' imprisonment and/or a $15,000 fine; for minor tranquilizers and less dangerous nonbarbiturate sedatives, imprisonment of up to three years and/or a fine of up to $10,000; for drug mixtures like cough medicines containing small amounts of codeine or other narcotics, up to one year in jail and/or a $5,000 fine. Time and fine are doubled for second offenders.

The law's weight falls most heavily on those selling to minors. When a person over 18 deals to someone *below* 21, first offense punishment is double that usually given; for narcotics dealers, as much as 30 years' imprisonment and/or $50,000 in fines. Second offenses receive *triple* the sentence ordinarily given.

Special exception is made in the case of a person caught distributing a small amount of marijuana to others at no profit to himself. Here, the offender is prosecuted as if he were a simple possessor, and may have his record erased as mentioned previously, if he is not over 21 and it is his first offense.

Enforcers are most concerned with the "big fish" of the drug world, so the new Act sets up special penalties for those convicted of "continuing criminal enterprise." When it can be proven that a person has engaged in drug business (from which a great deal of profit has come) involving a series of violations committed with five or more people, he will receive 10 years to life imprisonment and up to $100,000 in fines; any money made goes to the government. Second offenders receive double penalties.

The government may choose to label an individual over 21 being prosecuted for any drug offense as a ''dangerous drug offender'' if he is a continuing serious violator of drug laws for high personal profit. To protect the public from such a person, he may be imprisoned for up to 25 years, *besides* being sentenced for his original crime.

Illegally importing, or exporting, or smuggling controlled drugs carries a maximum sentence of 15 years in jail and/or a $25,000 fine for narcotics; and lower, but stiff, penalties for smuggling other drugs. For less serious offenses, such as improper record-keeping, or interfering with proper drug labeling, penalties range from fines as high as $25,000, to one year in jail and/or a $25,000 fine. This is true even for first offenders, if such an offense was committed with full knowledge of its criminal nature.

Legislators believe that with this updated penalty system, federal judges now really have much more flexibility than before, and can tailor sentences to each particular case, rather than prosecuting the young, often naïve drug offender and the hardened criminal under the same law.

The U.S. government never intended that its laws should provide the only basis for national drug control. Federal agencies have neither the time, manpower, nor funds to pursue every drug offender, and are generally more interested in large-scale illegal drug activity than in smaller crimes. Most of these smaller cases are still handled by state enforcers, offenders being tried under state and local laws that vary tremendously from state to state, and often are quite inconsistent. An offender may be prosecuted under both federal and state laws for the same crime, and receive a state penalty much heavier than the federal one. In some states, minor marijuana offenses are still punished by major jail terms. Some state laws have no corresponding federal law. Many states do not recognize the difference between narcotics and marijuana, regulate barbiturates without controlling amphetamines, or control only one major hallucinogen — usually LSD. Importantly, conditions in state and county jails, where the majority of "small" offenders serve their terms, are usually much worse than in federal penitentiaries.

The Comprehensive Drug Abuse Act authorizes over $160 million to be spent in rehabilitating drug abusers at various federal, state, and local centers. In 1966 the federal government also passed a Narcotics Rehabilitation Act, allowing certain addicts to be *committed* to treatment centers instead of being imprisoned. If the addict has already been convicted, he may, in some cases, be transferred from prison to a treatment center. Also, noncriminal addicts may *still* be committed by a judge for treatment, *involuntarily,* upon complaint of a relative. (They may also commit themselves voluntarily to such treatment.) At the state level, New York and California have also set up programs in which certain addicts are "sentenced" to treatment centers. This legislation is controversial; concern has been expressed for protecting the addict's constitutional rights from what some believe to be a mistaken application of legal power.

Alcohol is not officially classified or dealt with under the new legislation. Instead, it is controlled by a vast assortment of other regulations, mostly at state and local levels. Punishment for breaking these laws may range from a few days in jail or light fines for simple drunkenness, to heavy penalties for drunken driving. There is much debate today over whether it's legal to imprison a person simply for being drunk.

Many agencies of the federal government have been involved in drug control and research, with differing points of view and much duplication of work. A new agency was created in 1968, to consolidate much of this effort. It's called the Bureau of Narcotics and Dangerous Drugs (BNDD), and was formed by merging two smaller agencies, the Bureau of Narcotics (of the Treasury Department) and the Bureau of Drug Abuse Control (of the Food and Drug Administration). The BNDD is presently under the jurisdiction of the Justice Department.

The greatest responsibility of the BNDD is the enforcement of federal regulations controlling narcotics, marijuana, and Dangerous Drugs, working in close cooperation with state and local authorities. It plays a large role in setting standards and quotas for legal drug trade. The bureau also sets up educational programs to spread information on drug abuse, and gives specialized training to law enforcement officials as well as to pharmacists, chemists, and college officials. The BNDD conducts its own research, and consults with its Scientific Advisory Council, to determine what new drugs should be controlled.

Even adults not given to crusading wonder if controls might not eventually reach the point where they overstep the law's limits, and strike at basic constitutional rights: the right to privacy, the right to live your life the way you choose (assuming you hurt no one) regardless of whether the rest of society approves. Is it fair to place severe restrictions on drugs, without placing similar strong controls on the abuse of guns, cars, or cigarettes? Assuming that certain behavior is unacceptable to society, is punishment by jail or fine the best way to change this behavior? And what should be the response to laws that were written in fear, or are based on obvious misinformation?

By paying attention to these complicated, all-important issues, legal experts, physicians, public health officials, and enforcers have already begun working together to replace some of the outmoded laws that still exist. But simply throwing out all the laws, as some enthusiasts have proposed, is no more a solution to our drug dilemma than the mindless application of unreasonable force.

11

THE LOSERS
AND THE SURVIVORS

By now, you have an appreciation of the different
drugs on the scene today, why and how they are
abused, and some of the complicated medical, social,
and legal issues the drug scene has raised in
America.

Where do you go from here? Each of you is going
to have to make some decision about drugs, about
the role you want them to play in your life. What
about your future, if you do enter the drug scene?
What happens, for instance, to those people who
become so heavily dependent on drugs that nothing
else matters?

Just as any battle has its permanent casualties, so
does the struggle to grow psychologically from a

child who is totally dependent on others into an independent, mature adult, with a unique, definite system of values and beliefs. There have always been people who could not make the transition and who have lost this struggle.

Today's losers are often heads. It is hard to discover how large a part drugs have played in leading a loser away from forming a complete social and sexual identity, from being able to hold his own with dignity and self-respect as a worker, a lover, and eventually, a parent. As you have seen throughout this book, young people who become heads generally bring to the drug scene personalities already damaged, perhaps by poor economic and social conditions, problems with parents, or a combination of life stresses. It's debatable whether a person's downfall occurs because drugs enter his life, or whether drugs just happen to be the particular way a loser picks to go down for the count.

At any rate, once a loser drops out with drugs, there are many ways to stay out, many losing identities to "choose" from.

As a chronic head, a victim can go on drifting into and out of one drug scene after another, ending up as an overaged hippie scrounging his way through life, living only for the next high. His involvement may lead him into the world of crime, into dealing, pushing, or stealing. Inevitably, he can be arrested and imprisoned, exchanging the identity of head for criminal or convict.

Some heads end up playing the role of "psychi-

atric patient'': permanently freaked out, institution-
alized or barely managing to live outside of a hospital, like a tightrope walker in a state of fragile
emotional balance.

There are many other lives open to losers, and
different drugs to influence how they are lived: the
frequent job changes and marital conflict of the
chronic alcoholic; the sexual promiscuity and prostitution of the female heroin addict; the thieving of
the male heroinhead, the paranoia of the amphetamine abuser.

The final choice of the loser, the last and unredeem-
able identity is death — from overdose, assault, or
accident.

Luckily, for many young people, a heavy commitment to drugs is only temporary, and they manage to
survive the experience. Some of these survivors owe
their reentry into the pain and pleasure of life in the
real world to professional help — from ministers,
family doctors, teachers, mental health workers.
Many others survive without professional help,
working their way out of the corner they have
painted themselves into by lonely efforts to discover
what really counts instead of drugs. Sometimes, without realizing it, friends, and even those much down-
graded parents of the head, do valuable service just
by listening or being there to sweat out his troubles
with him.

Two distinct types of users who have been severely
drug dependent and then have given it up could be
called *acceptors* and *evolutionaries*.

After dropping into drug abuse, an acceptor resolves his revolt against his beliefs of his parents and the conventional views of society, and winds up accepting the same goals and values he was previously struggling against, though perhaps changing them a little according to his needs. If he has left school, he goes back. He stops drugs completely, or takes them only occasionally — at a party, for instance. He manages to lead a pretty well-adjusted life without stirring up waves or breaking new ground. Insofar as anyone can be happy in this anxiety-ridden modern world, he is fairly content and secure. Here is an example:

Stan is twenty-one years old and comes from an achievement-minded, middle-class home. In his second year of college, he became increasingly dissatisfied with "being like everyone else" and began to question his future career as a businessman working for his dad.

He started smoking marijuana and hashish, first over the weekends and then every day, until he was stoned most of his waking hours. He cut all of his classes and examinations. He took ten LSD trips. Finally, his grades got so bad that he decided to apply for a leave of absence.

He spent his next year in his father's business, living at home and seeing a psychiatrist. At this point, he met an old high school girl friend, fell in love with her again, became engaged, and reentered college. He is presently doing quite well.

He still plans to work in his dad's business when he graduates, but instead of staying in the office as an executive, he will travel and sell. He now smokes pot only occasionally. He believes that meeting his girl and falling in love were at least as responsible as his psychotherapy for bringing him back to a sense of what he really wanted.

An evolutionary is the kind of sensitive, talented young person who is particularly dissatisfied with himself and the world and is deeply dedicated to changing both constructively. Because of personal hangups, social pressures, or disgust with the hypocrisy of the adult world as he sees it, he may get seriously involved with drugs, especially the psychedelics. This is not simply because of what he is rebelling *against* but also because of what, with great intensity and passion he is searching *for:* a better way to live.

Sometimes, these young people become heads on the rebound, from experiences that force them to believe it's futile to try to change things. For instance, some of the early civil rights workers, as they grew increasingly depressed at the slowness of their progress to achieve equality for disadvantaged people, threw up their hands and turned to drugs.

Then, sooner or later, the evolutionary discovers that drugs are a dead end; that the promise of greater self-knowledge is not kept or that the bad effects outweigh any possibility for good. So he continues his fight for *evolution:* either to move the society forward, or really to get to know himself. But he proceeds *without drugs,* using other methods that vary from one person to another, depending on individual backgrounds and values. Like the acceptor, he may be helped by professionals, like psychiatrists and other youth workers, or he may go it alone.

The evolutionary may decide to seek growth through activism, dropping back in to work with the traditional political parties or the more conventional organizations devoted to improving the conditions of the poor, the exploited, and the downtrodden throughout our country or abroad, like VISTA, the Job Corps, or the Peace Corps.

Other evolutionaries will despair of ever bringing about positive movement within the system as it stands and will join radical or even revolutionary political movements. These evolutionaries advocate militancy and confrontation, and their efforts have become notorious in the past few years.

Others adopt an even more radical approach, because they believe that *nothing* can influence our society, and that even radical militant activity is, in a sense, "joining in the game." So they drop out even further to start their own society, going to live simply off the land, sharing the essentials in tribal groups. Examples are the farms, or *communes* that have sprung up as the drug scene in the cities has grown more vicious and sordid.

Young people who became disillusioned when they found that drugs could not take them far enough in their inner voyage of self-discovery have taken up

other forms of mind-expansion, techniques of meditation known and practiced for centuries by wise
men of the East. Such methods of achieving self-
knowledge were developed in places like India,
Japan, China and Tibet. Most of these teachers of
meditation stress that drug use is a "false road,"
granting only the temporary illusion of spiritual
growth.

Some have found the answer to their search by
returning to the religion of their childhood, altering
and expanding old teachings to meet their modern
view of things. Others find truth in philosophies, both
old and new.

Instead of letting drugs shape them, there are
talented young people who begin to use the tools of
art — music, poetry, prose, or painting, sculpture,
film — to mold and project their vision of life. And
some have gone from the drug scene to become scientists, devoted to expanding our knowledge of the
physical world.

Evolutionaries don't always go completely off
drugs. LSD and psychedelics are still taken in some
communes, although many forbid their use. But those
who are truly healthy have no problems with dependence, psychological or physical. Drugs no longer
provide the only road to happiness and self-confi-
dence, because they have found something more
durable.

No evolutionary has all the answers, although he
may insist that he has. You may not like the changes
that some of the more radical people are pushing, or

the way they are being pushed. And you may very well be right. Only time will tell in what direction our society will move. But as a group, whatever their interests, these young persons are a potent source for positive growth. And, what is most important, the evolutionary survivor has passed from a stage of drugged passivity to being really effective. Here are two examples:

Lonnie, a twenty-two year old, has lived in Harlem all his life. A dropout at sixteen, he started abusing barbiturates and amphetamines with occasional snorts of heroin. He was arrested several times for petty theft, put on probation, and continued getting into trouble. Three years later, he was deeply into drugs and leading a totally aimless life.

At this point he met a neighborhood youth worker at a basketball game, with whom he struck up a warm friendship. Gradually, through his relationship, he grew interested in his community and took a job with a local group helping people with housing complaints, while finishing high school at night.

Lonnie now attends college classes part-time and is heavily involved in many aspects of civil and political rights at the grass roots level. His abuse of drugs is finished; he is completely clean.

Zack, a twenty-three year old from a conventional suburban background, got attracted to the hippie scene in his last year of college. At the time he was having tremendous problems separating from his family. He started smoking marijuana, then moved on to LSD and other psychedelics. He barely scraped through his last year of college. Then, much to his family's despair, he moved into New York's East Village, where he continued taking drugs heavily, but also started working for an underground newspaper from time to time.

Then Zack had a terrifying, bad trip, his first after fifteen LSD experiences. He stopped acid altogether, and grew progressively less interested in drugs. He started writing poetry. To his surprise, his work was accepted and published in national magazines.

Now Zack still lives in the East Village and supports himself by doing short-order cooking in a local restaurant, but his basic interest is writing. He gets along better with his parents, who have come to be more accepting of his life.

Although it's unlikely, just on a statistical basis, that you will ever become a head, there's a lot you can learn from the experience of these survivors. For all of you, as you mature into adults, have to decide whether you want to live relatively simple "accepting" lives, keeping pretty much to the paths of your parents, or whether you are going to make the world a little different, to move us forward in newer and more creative directions.

There isn't anything wrong with just accepting things as they are, if that is what you want to do.

However, if you've got some of the evolutionary spirit in you, as have most young people, you should realize that the same methods of changing the world or exploring inner horizons that the evolutionary survivors turned to, after they found how meaningless or unfulfilling the drug scene really was, are all there, right now, waiting for you. You can pick up the tools, without having to undergo the torment, and horror, and the essential emptiness so many found with drugs instead of what they were really searching for.

Sure, drugs can give you kicks, make you feel high and happy, but there are other pleasures more enduring, more satisfying than any granted temporarily by chemical crutches. One of these is the pleasure of giving and receiving love. Many survivors claim that the belief that another person found them valuable and worthwhile is what really brought them back.

Unaided by drugs, the mind of man has reached into the depth of his own unconscious to create masterpieces, or soared into infinity to wrestle secrets from the stars. Don't underestimate the powers of your mind, and what it can accomplish on its own. All the vital answers to how you want to live your life are already deep within you, waiting only for the questions to be asked. You don't need drugs to find the answers, or ask the questions!

APPENDIX

DRUG DICTIONARY

Drug slang changes quickly and is different from place to place across the nation, so some of the terms may not be current when you read this.

Abuse: use of a drug in a way that departs from approved medical or social practice and which causes emotional or physical damage as well as unusual or antisocial behavior. A person who takes drugs in this way is an **abuser.**

Acapulco gold: a variety of top quality marijuana.

Acetaldehyde: a product formed in the body when alcohol is broken down by disulfiram. An extremely uncomfortable reaction occurs.

Acid: LSD.

Addiction: the state when the abuser is so physically and/or psychologically dependent on drugs that he cannot function without them, so that his life revolves around drug seeking and taking. The person is called an **addict.**

Alcoholic: a person addicted to alcohol. (See **Addiction.**)

Amies: slang term for amyl nitrate.

Amphetamines: the most widely abused group of pep pills, or stimulant drugs. They are all related to the chemical substance, amphetamine. The most popular amphetamines are called amphetamine (Benzedrine®), dextoamphetamine (Dexedrine®), and methamphetamine (Methedrine® or Desoxyn®).

Amyl nitrate: an inhalant legitimately used in heart disease. In abuse, sniffed to get high.

Anesthesia: medical term describing a state of insensitivity to pain; a drug that causes this state is called an **anesthetic.**

Antabuse®: a drug causing extreme discomfort after alcohol is taken; used to prevent drinking in alcoholics.

Artillery: homemade or stolen equipment for taking drugs by injection.

Bad trip: an unpleasant or frightening drug experience, usually with LSD.

Bag: what you like to do or are into; also, a package of drugs.

Bale: a pound of marijuana.

Bang: to inject a drug; also, a strong drug experience.

Barbiturates: a widely prescribed and abused group of sedatives, or sleep-producing chemicals.

Barbs: barbiturates.

Belladonna alkaloids: chemicals found in nature. **Scopolamine:** used in medicine for a combination of drowsiness and drying action on mucous membranes of the mouth, throat, and lungs; also in popular over-the-counter sleeping medication, combined with antihistamines and other drugs. **Stramonium:** used in over-the-counter preparations for asthma to ease difficult breathing. Abused for sedative effects.

Bennies: Benzedrine® tablets (an amphetamine).

Bhang: see **Cannabis.**

Big C: cocaine.

Blasted: strongly affected or influenced by a drug.

Blow a stick, smoke a joint: smoke a marijuana cigarette.

Blow your mind: to have an intense experience with or without drugs; also to go insane, with or without drugs.

Blue birds, blue devils, blue heavens, blues: Amytal® capsules (a barbiturate).

Blue velvet: a combination of paregoric (opium dissolved in alcohol) and an antihistamine (an anti-allergy drug with sedative properties), taken intravenously.

Bluies: morphine pills.

Bombido, bombita, bottle: liquid Benzedrine® for injection (an amphetamine).

Boo: marijuana.

Boost: to steal or shoplift.

Bread: money.

Bummer: a bad trip or an extremely unpleasant or frightening experience from having taken a drug, usually LSD or another psychedelic. May also be used to refer to any bad experience.

Burned, busted: arrested.

Buttons: parts of the peyote cactus used for a psychedelic experience.

Caffeine: a mild stimulant found in coffee.

Can: about an ounce of marijuana.

Candy: barbiturates; sometimes, cocaine.

Cannabis: a tall, leafy plant (*cannabis sativa*) whose resin has psychoactive properties. Cannabis preparations include (from strongest to weakest) **hashish, charas, bhang, ganja,** and **marijuana.**

Cap: a capsule of powdered drug; also, a small packet of heroin.

Cartwheels: Benzedrine® tablets (an amphetamine).

Charas: see **Cannabis.**

Charlie, coke: cocaine.

Chloral hydrate: a nonbarbiturate sleep-producing (sedative) drug.

Chromosomes: messengers of heredity found in every body cell. (Doctors fear that LSD, by causing chromosome changes, might cause user's children to be born dead or deformed.)

Cibas: Doriden® tablets (a sedative).

Cirrhosis: a serious liver disease common in alcoholics.

Clean: off drugs.

Coast-to-coast, copilot: long-acting Benzedrine® capsules (amphetamines).

Cocaine: a powerful stimulant drug, originally extracted from the leaves of the coca bush. Abuse can produce a state of dependence similar to, but often stronger than, that produced by amphetamines.

Codeine: a narcotic derived from opium; prescribed legally for relief of pain, or commonly for cough, in syrup; can be abused like other narcotics.

Cokey or **coke head:** cocaine abuser.

Cold turkey: stopping drug abuse suddenly without the help of medication; usually applied to going off heroin.

Coma: a deep state of unconsciousness in which the vital functions are slowed down tremendously.

Come down: to end a drug experience.

Communes: groups of people who live together outside of the mainstream of life.

Connection: a person who supplies drugs, usually heroin.

Cop: to buy or purchase.

Cool it: to keep quiet or calm.

Crash: to come down suddenly and painfully from a drug experience; to fall into a deep sleep after using a drug or withdrawing from a drug; also, to stay somewhere after running away from home.

Crash-pad: place to stay in an emergency or after running away from home.

Crystals: crystalline form of Methedrine® used for injection (an amphetamine).

Cut: to dilute a drug with some other substance, in order to make it go further and make more money from its sale.

Dangerous Drugs: any number of barbiturates, amphetamines or hallucinogens which are officially recognized by federal law as being harmful to physical or mental health.
Dealer: a drug seller.
Deck: an envelope containing heroin.
Delirium: a temporary state of mental disturbance, characterized by confusion, disordered speech, and often hallucinations.
Delirium Tremens (DT's): a serious mental disturbance with shaking of hands, great excitement, and hallucinations, seen in chronic alcoholics and often related to withdrawal from alcohol after a binge.
Delusion: a false or weird belief that the deluded person is absolutely convinced is true. A common delusion is one of persecution, in which the person feels he is being seriously threatened by people.
Depressant: a drug that causes slowing down of activity in various organs of the body, especially in the brain and nervous system.
Depression: may refer to a physical and mental slowing down due to a depressant drug, such as a barbiturate, which causes drowsiness, and in high doses, a state of deep sleep from which the abuser cannot be aroused; also refers to an emotional state of deep sadness and despair, accompanied by feelings of worthlessness, helplessness, and even suicide.
Dexies: Dexedrine® tablets (an amphetamine).
Dextroamphetamine: see **Amphetamines.**
Dime bag: a ten-dollar package of drugs.
DMT (dimethyltryptamine): a psychedelic drug, usually smoked, that produces a short, intense experience similar to that produced by LSD.
Do: to take a drug; to have a drug experience.
Dolls: pills or capsules.
Dollys: methadone, a synthetic narcotic (trade name: Dolophine®).
DOM: the chemical name for the active ingredient in most doses of STP.
Down: a barbiturate.
Drop: to swallow a drug, to take a drug.
Drug: a substance that, when introduced into the body, changes the way the body works.

Ethyl alcohol: a liquid with a stinging taste; the intoxicating drug in any alcoholic beverage.
Euphoria: a state of pleasure and joy.
Eye opener: an amphetamine; also refers to an alcoholic's first drink of the morning.

Feds: federal narcotics' agents.
Fix: an injection of a drug, usually heroin or other narcotic.
Flashback: a spontaneous recurrence of an LSD experience when off the drug.
Flip out, freak out: to have a bad experience or to feel as if you are going crazy, on or off drugs; also refers to a good or pleasurable emotional reaction to an experience, as ''That really flipped me out!''
Floating, flying: feeling good under a drug's influence.
Footballs: Benzedrine® tablets (an amphetamine).
Formication: unpleasant sensation of something crawling on or in the skin.

Gage: marijuana.
Ganja: see **Cannabis.**
Getting off: injecting heroin.
Gin, goofy dust: cocaine.

Goofball: a barbiturate-amphetamine combination; less frequently, a barbiturate alone.

Grass: marijuana.

Gun: a hypodermic needle.

Guru: slang term for a person who supposedly guides an LSD initiate on his way.

H, harry, horse: heroin.

Hallucinate: to see, hear, feel, or smell something that isn't really there. Such an experience is called an **hallucination.**

Hallucinogen: a mind-influencing or mind-manifesting drug; a psychedelic.

Hash: hashish.

Hashish: see **Cannabis.**

Hay: marijuana.

Head: someone whose entire life centers around a drug or drugs; **pot head:** someone heavily into marijuana; **acid head:** the same, with LSD; **meth head:** the same, with Methedrine®; **glue head:** the same, with glue.

Head shop: a store selling psychedelic paraphernalia.

Hearts: Dexedrine® or Benzedrine® tablets (amphetamines).

Heavenly blues: a variety of morning glory seeds, with LSD-like substances.

Hepatitis: a serious inflammation of the liver, often spread from one addict to another by contaminated needles.

Heroin: a powerful narcotic, the most widely abused of its class today.

High: a pleasurable feeling on drugs.

Hooked: addicted to drugs, usually heroin or other narcotic.

Hustler: a prostitute.

Hung up: bothered by problems; sometimes used to indicate a heavy dependence on drugs.

Hydromorphone: a semi-synthetic narcotic, derived from opium (Dilaudid®).

Hypnotic: a drug that induces sleep.

Illusion: a false perception or interpretation (mistaking clothing thrown over a chair for a burglar).

Inhalants: a group of substances found in household or industrial products —airplane glue, lighter fluid, gasoline, shoepolish, deodorant sprays, cleaning fluid—containing such drugs as toluene, naptha, benzene, and carbon tetrachloride. When sniffed, they produce a high, giddy state.

Joint: a marijuana cigarette.

Jolly beans: amphetamine pills.

Joy pop: an occasional use of heroin by a nonaddict; term sometimes used with contempt by heroin addicts.

Jug: liquid Benzedrine® for injection (an amphetamine).

Junk: heroin or other drugs.

Junkie: a heroin or narcotics addict.

Kick the habit: to stop taking drugs, usually heroin.

Kicks: good feelings from drugs.

Kilo: a kilogram, 2.2 pounds.

LSD (D-lysergic acid diethlamide): the most widely publicized psychedelic, hallucinogenic, or mind-expanding drug. Extremely small amounts can produce an intense experience often characterized by hallucinations, mood

changes, disturbances in feelings of reality, and other emotional reactions.
Lid: about an ounce of marijuana.

M, monkey: morphine.
Mainline: to take drugs by intravenous injection.
Man: police or narcotics' agent.
Manicure: strong marijuana.
Marijuana: the dried leaves and flowering tops of the cannabis plant (*cannabis sativa*). (See also **Cannabis.**)
Mellow yellow: a preparation made from banana skins, wrongly supposed to have psychedelic effects.
Meperidine: a totally synthetic narcotic (trade name: Demerol®).
Mescaline: a drug found in the peyote cactus; also, laboratory-made. It produces a psychedelic experience somewhat similar to that produced by LSD.
Meth: Methedrine® (an amphetamine).
Methadone: a totally synthetic narcotic used in the treatment of heroin addicts (trade name: Dolophine®).
Mike: microgram (measure for dosage of LSD); one millionth of a gram.
Milligram (mg.): a common measure of drug dosage: one thousandth of a gram.
Morning glory seeds: seeds of the common flower. Some varieties have LSD-like properties.
Mushrooms: psilocybin or psilocin, hallucinogens obtained from mushrooms, or the mushrooms themselves.

Narcotic: a drug producing a combination of pain-killing and peace and calm. For the potential addict, narcotics give an intense experience of joy and pleasure. Principal narcotic drugs: morphine, heroin, codeine, opium.
Narc: a narcotics' agent.
Nembies, nemmies, nimmies: Nembutal® capsules (a barbiturate).
Nickel bag: five dollars worth of drugs.
Nitrous oxide: an inhalant with anesthetic properties, originally called "laughing gas" and used in dentistry as well as to get high.
Nod: a sleepy state under the influence of drugs, usually heroin; **on the nod:** under the influence of drugs, usually heroin.
Nutmeg: a common household spice with psychedelic properties.

OD: an overdose of drugs.
Opium: a narcotic obtained from the opium poppy and from which various narcotics are extracted; widely abused in the East.
Oranges: Dexedrine® tablets (an amphetamine).

Pack: a packet of drugs, usually heroin.
Panama red: a top quality marijuana, rich in THC.
Paper: a doctor's prescription, also known as "scrip."
Paraldehyde: a nonbarbiturate sleep-producing (sedative) drug.
Paranoid: characterized by extreme suspiciousness (a psychiatric term).
Peaches: Benzedrine® tablets (an amphetamine).
Peanuts: barbiturates.
Pearly gates: a variety of morning glory seeds, with LSD-like substance.
Pep pills: see **Stimulants; Amphetamines.**
Peyote: a cactus whose buds produce a psychedelic experience.
Phennies: phenobarbital tablets (a barbiturate).
Physical dependence: a condition in which a drug user, upon stopping the use of a drug, experiences uncomfortable and even violent physical (with-

drawal) symptoms.

Point: a needle used for drug injection.

Poppers: slang term for amyl nitrate.

Pot: marijuana.

Preludin®: a drug related to the amphetamines, widely abused for its stimulant properties.

Psilocybin, psilocin: psychedelic drugs found in mushrooms; also laboratory-made, which produce an experience similar to an LSD experience.

Psychedelic: mind manifesting or mind altering (slang: cool, with it, swinging, hip). The hallucinogenic or mind-expanding drugs, such as LSD, mescaline, or psilocybin, are also called psychedelics.

Psychoactive: having the power to change feelings, emotions, and sometimes behavior.

Psychological dependence: a condition in which the user, upon stopping a drug, experiences an emotional craving or need that may vary in strength from mild to severe.

Psychosis: a form of severe mental illness, in which the person loses touch with reality, and may experience hallucinations and delusions.

Pusher: one who sells drugs.

Quill: a folded piece of stiff paper or cardboard that is used for sniffing heroin, cocaine, or other drugs.

Redbirds, red devils, reds: Seconal® capsules (a barbiturate).

Reefer: a marijuana cigarette.

Roach: the butt of a marijuana cigarette.

Roses: Benzedrine® tablets (an amphetamine).

Run: a prolonged period of heavy use of a drug; same as jag.

Scag, Smack, Shmeck: heroin.

Schizophrenia: a type of mental illness characterized by loss of contact with reality and disintegration of personality.

Scopolamine: see **Belladonna alkaloids.**

Score: to find a drug supply.

Seccies, seggies: Seconal® capsules (a barbiturate).

Sedatives: any drug that exerts a generally depressant effect on the nervous system, producing relaxation, calm, and sleep. Sedatives have high abuse potential, are known as downs, and can lead to severe physical and psychological dependence. Barbiturates are the best known. Other sedatives include chloral hydrate, paraldehyde, Nodular®, Placidyl®, Doriden®, Valmid®. Antihistamines, drugs found in cold tablets, also have mild sedative effects and are occasionally abused.

Shoot, shoot up: to take drugs by injection.

Shooting gallery: a place addicts go to take drugs, especially heroin.

Side effects: effects from a drug that have no relation to results drug is being used for; usually not desirable.

Skin pop: to inject drugs underneath the skin.

Snort: to inhale drug powder, such as heroin, amphetamine, cocaine.

Snow, snuff: cocaine.

Spansule: a time-release capsule containing a drug.

Speed: crystalline form of Methedrine® used for injection (an amphetamine); can refer to any amphetamine. **Speeding:** taking Methedrine®.

Speedball: a combinataion of heroin and cocaine or an amphetamine.

Spike: a needle used for drug injection.

Stash: a hidden supply of drugs, or a personal supply.

Stick: a marijuana cigarette.

Stimulant: a drug that increases or excites activity in various body organs including the brain and central nervous system. (See also **Amphetamines.**)

Stoned: under the influence of drugs.

STP: a synthetic psychedelic briefly popular in the drug underground, actually a chemical known as DOM. (See also **DOM**).

Stramonium: see **Belladonna alkaloids.**

Stretch: to dilute a drug. (See also **Cut.**)

Strung out: heavily into a drug or drugs; to feel a craving for a drug.

Strychnine: a highly poisonous white crystalline drug used to cut heroin, which it resembles in appearance.

Stuff: marijuana.

Sugar: LSD.

Synethesia: the condition in which one kind of sensation is converted to another. Example: music is ''felt''; sound is ''seen'' on an LSD trip.

Tea: marijuana.

THC (tetrahydracannabinols): the chemical constituents in cannabis that cause psychedelic effects; laboratory-made by illicit drug manufacturers.

Tolerance: a condition existing when a user requires increasing amounts of a drug to produce the original physical and/or psychological effect.

Tooies: Tuinal® capsules. A combination of Amytal® and Seconal®.

Tranquilizers: drugs used to control anxiety, tension, restlessness, and other emotional reactions. So-called minor tranquilizers—Miltown® (or Equanil® or meprobamate), Valium®, Librium®—are usually prescribed for mild symptoms, have high abuse potential, create physical and psychological dependence. Major tranquilizers include Thorazine®, Mellaril®, Stelazine®, and are generally used in more severe emotional conditions, including the treatment of bad trips caused by drugs like LSD.

Trip: a drug experience, especially with psychedelic drugs like LSD.

Truck driver: an amphetamine.

Turn on: to take drugs; to get excited about and interested in something.

25: LSD.

Up: an amphetamine.

Wake up: an amphetamine.

Weed: marijuana.

Whites: Benzedrine® tablets (an amphetamine).

Wired: drug dependent.

Withdrawal symptoms: uncomfortable, even violent physical and/or emotional reactions, occurring when a drug is suddenly taken away.

Yellows, yellow jackets: Nembutal® capsules (a barbiturate).

HELP: TREATMENT CENTERS

On the following pages is a list of the many facilities throughout the nation that are involved in treating those with drug problems, or in spreading information about drugs and drug abuse. This list is as up to date as possible, but if you find no listing for your area or state, check with your local or state department of health, private physician, or clergyman to find out if a treatment agency has been set up since this book was published.

Space does not permit a description of the services each agency provides. Many treatment facilities are geared to help people with heroin or other narcotic problems only. However, there are an increasing number of places where people who have problems with other drugs can find help.

ARIZONA
Maricopa County Hosp.
3435 W. Durango St.
Phoenix 85009

Teen Challenge
21 W. Willetta
Phoenix 85003

CALIFORNIA
The Bridge Back, Inc.
5505 S. Central
Los Angeles 90065

Cal. Rehabilitation Ctr.
Box 841
Corona 91720

El Projecto de Barrio
13700 Paxton St.
Pacoima 91331

Immediate Psychiatric
Aid Center (IMPAC)
San Francisco Gen. Hosp.
22nd and Potrero
San Francisco 94110

LUCHA (League of
United Citizens to
Help Addicts)
Euclid Hgts. Com. Ctr.
3045 Whittier Blvd.
Los Angeles 90023

Narcotic Addiction
Outpatient Program
1102 S. Crenshaw Blvd.
Los Angeles 90019

Narcotic Prevention Proj.
507 Enchandia St.
Los Angeles

Synanon
1215 Clay St.
Oakland 94612

Teen Challenge
2263 S. Hobart
Los Angeles 90018

COLORADO
Colo. State Hosp.
1600 W. 24th St.
Pueblo 81003

CONNECTICUT
Blue Hills Hosp.
51 Coventry St.
Hartford 06112

Conn. Mental Health Ctr.
Drug Dependence Unit
34 Park St.
New Haven 06519

Conn. Valley Hosp.
Silver St.
Middletown 06457

Norwich State Hosp.
Rte. 12 Box 508
Norwich 06360

DELAWARE
Wilmington Medical Ctr.
501 W. 14th St.
Wilmington 19801

Wilmington Mental
Health Clinic
1213 Walnut
Wilmington 19801

DISTRICT OF COLUMBIA
Community Mental
Health Ctrs.

Areas A, B, C
1905 E. St.
Area D, Dix Bldg.

St. Elizabeth's Hosp.
Narcotic Addiction
Treatment Ctr.
1825 13th St., N.W.
Washington 20009

ILLINOIS
Drug Abuse Program
Dept. Mental Health
5801 S. Ellis Ave.
Chicago 60637
(with Univ. of Chicago)
Washington 20002

Gateway House
Foundation
4800 S. Ellis Ave.
Chicago 60615

Teen Challenge
315 S. Ashland
Chicago 60607

IOWA
Broadlawns Polk
County Hosp.
18th and Hickman Rd.
Des Moines 50314

KENTUCKY
U.S. Public Health
Service Hosp.
Box 2000
Lexington 40501

MARYLAND
Nat. Inst. Mental Health
Barlow Bldg.
Chevy Chase 20015

Crownsville State Hosp.
Crownsville 21032

MASSACHUSETTS

Boston City Hosp.
818 Harrison Ave.
Boston 02118

Boston State Hosp.
591 Morton St.
Boston 02124

Drug Addiction Unit
20 Whittier St.
Boston 02120

MICHIGAN

Synanon
8344 E. Jefferson Ave.
Detroit 48214

Teen Challenge
4600 Lovett Box 5992
Detroit 48210

MINNESOTA

Willmar State Hosp.
Box 1128
Willmar 56201

MISSISSIPPI

Miss. State Hosp.
Whitfield 39193

MISSOURI

Archway House
5650 Pershing Ave.
St. Louis 63112

Teen Challenge
Box 4915
St. Louis 63108

Univ. of Mo.
Inst. of Psychiatry
5400 Arsenal St.
St. Louis 63139

NEBRASKA

Hastings State Hosp.
Ingleside 68953

NEW JERSEY

Drug Addiction Rehabilitation Enterprise
236 6th Ave.
Newark 07107

Mt. Carmel Guild Narcotics Rehabilitation
107 Central Ave.
Newark 07102

N.J. Neuro-
Psychiatric Inst.
Newark (Outpatient)
Princeton (Resident)

N.J. Rehabilitation
Comm. Narcotics Proj.
19 N. Harrison Ct.,
2nd Fl.
East Orange 07017

The New Well
273 18th St.
Newark 07103

Odyssey House
61 Lincoln Park
Newark 07112

Union County
Narcotics Clinic
43 Rahway Ave.
Elizabeth 07202

NEW MEXICO

Bernalillo Cnty. (U.
N.M.) Comprehensive
Com. Mental Health
Ctr.
1007 Stanford, N.E.
Albuquerque 87106

NEW YORK

Addicts Rehabilitation
Ctr. Manhattan Christian Reformed Ch.
253 W. 123rd St.
New York 10027

Anchor House, Inc.
976 Park Place
Brooklyn 11213

Alateen
Box 192 Madison Sq. Sta.
New York 10011

Alcoholics Anonymous
(AA)
337 E. 33rd St.
New York 10016

Amer. Social Health
Assn.
1740 Broadway
New York 10019

Bellevue Hosp.
550 1st Ave.
New York 10016

Bronx Mun. Hosp. Ctr.
Morris Pk. & Seminole
Bronx 10461

Brooklyn-Cumberland
Medical Ctr.
39 Auburn Place
Brooklyn 11205

Civic Ctr. Clinic
44 Willoughby St.
Brooklyn 11201

Community and Narcotics Action Ctr.
997 E. 156th St.
Bronx 10455

Community Organization
on Narcotics Educ.
516 Sutter Ave.
Brooklyn 11207

Community Program Ctr.
Narcotics Unit
922 Southern Blvd.
Bronx 14059

Daytop Village, Inc.
450 Bayview Ave.
Prince's Bay
Staten Island 10309

Encounter, Inc.
150 Spring St.
New York 10013

Exodus House
304 E. 103rd St.
New York 10029

Ft. Green Vocational
and Rehabilitation
League, Inc.
113 Myrtle Ave.
Brooklyn 11201

Gracie Square Hosp.
420 E. 76th St.
New York 10021

Greenwich House
27 Barrow St.
New York 10014

Harlem Hosp. Ctr.
532 Lenox Ave.
New York 10027

Interfaith Hosp. of
Queens
175-10 88th Ave.
Jamaica 11432

Kings Park State Hosp.
Kings Park 11754

Lower Eastside Info.
Service Ctr.
165 E. Broadway
New York 10002

Manhattan State Hosp.
Drug Addiction Research
Ward's Island 10035

Metropolitan Hosp.
1901 1st Ave.
New York 10029

Middletown State Hosp.
Box 1453
Middletown 10940

Narcotic Addiction
Control Comm.
(NACC)
Executive Park South
Stuyvesant Plaza
Albany 12203

Nassau County Drug
Abuse and Addiction
Comm. (Topic House)
719 Kenwood Ave.
Westbury, L.I. 11590

Neighborhood United
Teams Society
Ch. of the Open Door
201 Gold St.
Brooklyn 11201

N.Y. State Dept. Mental
Hygiene Aftercare
Clinic
39 E. 17th St.
New York 10003

Northwest Bronx Com.
on Narcotics Educ.
3029 Godwin Terrace
Bronx 10463

Odyssey House
309 E. 6th St.
New York 10004

Project NORA
1179 Boston Rd.
Bronx 10456

Quaker Com. on Social
Rehabilitation, Inc.
135 Christopher St.
New York 10014

Reality House
205 W. 145th St.
New York 10039

Rochester Mental
Health Ctr.
1425 Portland Ave.
Rochester 14621

Salvation Army,
Women's Correctional
Services
233 E. 17th St.
New York 10003

Synanon
35 Riverside Dr.
New York 10023

Teen Challenge
444 Clinton Ave.
Brooklyn 11238

University Hosp.
560 1st Ave.
New York 10016

The Village Haven
228 W. 15th St.
New York 10011

OHIO

Yellowsprings Encounter
Yellowsprings 45387

OREGON

Dammasch State Hosp.
Wilsonville 97070

Ore. State Hosp.
Station A
Salem 97201

PENNSYLVANIA

Inst. of Alcoholism,
Narcotic Addiction and
Compulsive Gambling
915 Corinthian Ave.
Philadelphia 19130

Narcotic Addict Treat-
ment Program, West
Phila. Mental Health
Consortium
Box 8076

Philadelphia 19101
Teen Challenge
Box 98

Rehrersburg 19550
Woodville Ctr.
Carnegie 15106

PUERTO RICO

Centro de Investigaciones
Sobre la Addicion
Edificio J.
Hospital de Psiquiatria
Rio Piedras
Hogar Nueva Esperanza
Vega Alta 00762

RHODE ISLAND

Dept. of Social Welfare
Mental Hygiene Services
333 Grotto Ave.
Providence 12906

Marathon House
Fish Hill Rd.
Coventry 02816

TEXAS

Clinical Research Ctr.
3150 Horton Rd.
Fort Worth 76119

The Patrician Movement
1249 S. St. Marys
San Antonio 78210

Teen Challenge
110 Commerce St.
Fort Worth 76102
(Two residence houses:
for girls in Fort Worth;
boys in Dallas)

HELP: DIRECT-LINE ASSISTANCE

ARIZONA
The Listening Post (Phoenix)
602-939-1453
Open Line (Tucson) 602-327-6681

CALIFORNIA
Campus Communication Center
(San Francisco State) 415-469-1100
415-421-0943
HELP Unit (San Francisco) Office:
415-421-9850; Night: 415-387-3575,
Mobile Unit: 415-954-7304
Hot Line (Los Angeles) 213-666-1015
Message Information Center
(San Diego) 714-232-6621
Palo Alto Exchange 415-327-9008
Switchboards: (Berkeley)
415-549-0649; (Chico) 916-342-7546;
(Contra Costa) 415-933-9800; (Oakland) East, 415-532-2134, West,
415-836-3013; (San Jose)
408-295-2938; (San Francisco)
415-387-3575, 415-861-5460,
415-836-3040; (San Rafael)
415-456-5300; (Santa Barbara)
805-968-3564; (Santa Cruz)
408-426-8500; (Univ. of Calif.,
Davis) 916-752-3495

COLORADO
Hip Help Center (Denver)
303-222-3344
Turnstile (Denver) 303-623-3445

DISTRICT OF COLUMBIA
Washington Switchboard
202-667-4684

FLORIDA
Center for Dialog (Miami)
305-634-7741

IOWA
Blackhawk Information Center
(Waterloo) 319-234-9365

MASSACHUSETTS
Boston Switchboard 617-246-2455
Project PLACE (Boston)
617-246-2455

MICHIGAN
Canterbury House (Ann Arbor)
313-665-0606
The Listening Ear (East Lansing)
517-337-1717

MINNESOTA
Youth Emergency Service
(Minneapolis) 612-338-7588

MISSOURI
The Ecstatic Umbrella (Kansas
City) 816-561-4524

NEW MEXICO
Switchboard (Arroyo Seco)
505-758-4288

NEW JERSEY
United Church Presbyterian
(Warren) 201-469-5044

NEW YORK
Hot Lines (Albany) 518-474-8166, referals to 17 state centers:
518-457-4176; (Binghamton)
607-722-5383; (Buffalo) 716-882-0800;
(Nassau-Suffolk counties)
516-249-7142; (New York City); (all
night) 212-787-7900; (Bronx)
212-588-4964; (Central Manhattan)
212-799-6940; (Harlem) 212-534-2400,
212-427-6868; (Lower East Side)
212-673-3770; (Queens) 212-739-1130;
(Rochester) 716-454-4320; (Syracuse)
315-474-5951; (Utica) 315-735-9502

OHIO
Community Information Service
(Cleveland) 614-781-2944
Switchboard (Columbus) 614-294-6378

OREGON
Outside-In (Portland) 503-223-4121
Switchboard (Portland) 503-224-0313

PENNSYLVANIA
Powellton Trouble Center
(Philadelphia) 215-382-6472

TEXAS
Switchboard (Houston) 713-228-6072

WASHINGTON
Open Door (Seattle) 206-524-7404

WISCONSIN
HELP (Milwaukee) 414-273-5959

FOREIGN
Binary Information Transfer
(London W2, England) 01-229-8219
Vancouver Crisis Center (Vancouver,
B.C., Canada) 604-733-1171

BIBLIOGRAPHY

For additional information on drugs, refer to the reading materials suggested below.

BOOKS

Alpert, R., Cohen, S., Schiller, L., *LSD*. New York: New American Library, 1966.

Barber, B., *Drugs and Society*. New York: Russell Sage, 1967.

Blakeslee, A., *What You Should Know About Drugs and Narcotics*. New York: Associated Press, 1969.

Blum, R. H., and Associates, *Utopiates; The Use and Users of LSD*. New York: Atherton Press, 1964.

Carey, J. T., *The College Drug Scene*. Englewood Cliffs, N.J.: Prentice-Hall (Spectrum Books S-196), 1968.

Chein, I., and Others, *The Road to H: Narcotics, Delinquency and Social Policy*. New York: Basic Books, 1964.

Cohen, S., *The Beyond Within: The LSD Story*. New York: Atheneum, 1964.

Coles, R., *The Grass Pipe*. Boston: Little, Brown & Co., 1969.

DeRopp, R. S., *Drugs and the Mind*. New York: Grove Press (Evergreen Black Cat #BC-7), 1957.

Goldstein, R., *One in Seven: Drugs on Campus*. New York: Walker & Co., 1966.

Hentoff, N., *A Doctor Among the Addicts*. Chicago: Rand McNally, 1968.

Hyde, M. O., ed., *Mind Drugs*. New York: McGraw Hill, 1968.

Kenniston, K., *The Uncommitted: Alienated Youth in American Society*. New York: Dell Publishing Co., 1967.

Louria, D., *The Drug Scene*. New York: McGraw-Hill, 1968.

Nowlis, H. H., *Drugs on the College Campus*. New York: Anchor Books, 1969.

Schaap, O., *Turned On*. New York: New American Library, 1968.

Solomon, D., ed., *The Marijuana Papers*. New York: New American Library (Signet Books), 1968.

Sokolow, M., and Louria, D., *Nightmare Drugs*. New York: Pocket Books (#10157), 1966.

Stafford, P. G. and Golightly, B. H., *LSD: The Problem-Solving Psychedelic*. New York: Award Books (A221 SK), 1967.

PAMPHLETS AND OTHER MATERIAL

The Attack. (Free). Published quarterly by the N.Y. State Narcotic Addiction Control Commission, Executive Park South, Albany, N.Y. 12203.

Darkness on Your Doorstep. Los Angeles County Dept. of Community Services, 1851 South West Moreland Ave., Los Angeles, Cal. 90006.

Drug Abuse, Escape to Nowhere. Published by Smith, Kline and French Laboratories, 1967. Available from NEA-Publications and Sales, 1201 W. 16th St. Washington, D.C. 20036.

Drugs and The Young. Time Education Program, 1970. ($1.50, 1-9 copies; $1.00, 10 or more copies.) Time-Life Building, Rockefeller Center, New York, N.Y. 10020.

Hooked. Public Health Service Publication #1610, 1967. National Institute of Mental Health, U.S. Government Printing Office, Washington, D.C. 20402.

Saltman, Jules, *What We Can Do About Drug Abuse*. New York: Public Affairs Pamphlet #390, 1966.

For many free pamphlets on drugs write to: Public Information Branch, National Institute of Mental Health, Chevy Chase, Md. 20203.

INDEX